DATE DUE FOR RETURN

ſ

THE
FIRST HUNDRED
ROAD MOTORS

R. W. KIDNER

THE OAKWOOD PRESS
1950

DEDICATED

to the memory of the men who made and drove the first hundred road motors, and especially to :—

SIR JAMES ANDERSON, who persevered in building steam carriages from 1824 to 1850, although success constantly eluded him.

LT./COL. FRANCIS MACERONE, who loved quick motion, and in 1832 pawned his last watch to buy a sack of coke for a drive out to Windsor.

G. F. G. DE VIGNE, who in 1863 discovered that the police did not interfere with motorists if they were wearing firemen's helmets.

JAMES MAYNARD, who at Greenwich Police Court in 1867 was the first to advance the theory that for motorists ignorance of the law is a complete defence. (Fined 5s.).

AUTHOR'S NOTE

Because the personalities who brought about the emancipation of motoring from prohibitive legislation in 1896 were both colourful and vociferous, the long history of road motors leading up to that happy event tends to be forgotten. There cannot be alive to-day more than a handful of men who, as children, gaped at the passing of any of the first hundred road motors. It is time these fading memories were revived. By gathering together all available material from contemporary sources I have tried to establish the identity of the first hundred road motors, and briefly to infuse them and their designers again with life. I have avoided copying long extracts from biographies and other works that can be referred to fairly easily, and concentrated upon presenting fully the scraps of information culled from less easily-available sources. Much that appears here appears in no other book.

The book is addressed primarily to students of transport history, but anyone to whom the eager individuality of Victorian days appeals will find it of interest. To us in this age of rationalisation it seems that then the world of industry was very young, and youth has its special charms.

R.W.K.

South Godstone,
February, 1949.

THE FIRST HUNDRED ROAD MOTORS

§ 1 *Pre-History* (1668-1789)

When the thread of time changed from its gay Regency colours to the sombre but more decent hues of Early Victorian days, the first few pages of the history of mechanical transport had already been written. The faint and faded scribbles of a score of mediaeval inventors, telling of their cars driven by wind and hand, were followed by brief mentions of the model steam-cars of the Jesuit Father Verbiest in 1668, and of Papin of Cassel in 1698.

Overleaf came the story of the first full-sized vehicle to move itself by steam, made by Nicholas James Cugnot in Paris in 1769. Time has effaced many of the details, but we know that it was run in Paris in the presence of the Duc de Choiseul, General Gribeauval (First Inspector-General of Artillery), Count de Saxe, and others ; that it knocked down a wall, and that orders were given for another machine to be built, to carry cannon. This second engine was built in 1771. Some say it never ran, others that it overturned near the Madeleine and was " arrested " as a nuisance. There is also a possibility that it was only the 1769 machine improved. At all events, it seems certain that this was the vehicle that now reposes in the Conservatoire des Arts et Metiers. It is of crude construction, with a pot-shaped copper boiler, containing two flues, and a two-cylinder* single-acting engine, both mounted on the single-wheeled fore-carriage. The reason for this design no doubt lay in the fact that the differential had not yet been invented, and without this the driving of the rear axle presented difficulties ; but it must necessarily have made the vehicle extremely unstable.

Ten years later, it is said, a certain Charles Dallery was running an amphibious steam-vehicle, a boat fitted with wheels, in Amiens : no details survive. It was not uncommon for inventors to seek to run before they could walk, and Dallery was not alone, for Oliver Evans ran just such an amphibious vehicle in America in 1804.

In England, James Watt's ingenious foreman, William Murdock, was building model steam-cars of a fair size. One† was running along the roads of Redruth in Cornwall in 1784, and this is still in existence. Historians are not agreed upon whether Murdock built more than one, but it seems unlikely that he could have built such an eminently practical machine without some previous less successful attempts. Boulton and Watt disapproved of their employee's

---

* 13-inch diameter. Connecting-rods pushing downwards drove ratchets on the front wheel.

† Cyl. $\frac{3}{4}$ by $2\frac{1}{8}$ in., driving wheels $9\frac{1}{4}$ in.

mind being taken off his pumping engines, and while he was on his way to London to show the model, he was met by Boulton near Exeter and persuaded to return to Cornwall.

Thus the practical development of the motor-car was delayed for twenty years.

Watt himself had taken out patents to cover steam-carriage construction, in which he postulated that a car containing two people would require an engine with a cylinder 7 in. diameter by 12 in. stroke, making sixty strokes per minute : a very accurate forecast as it later turned out. In a letter to Boulton in 1786 Watt wrote : "I have one (steam-carriage) of some size under hand . . ." He seems not to have pursued the matter : is the clue to this contained in another remark on motor-construction to his partner : ". . . and if it cannot be secured (i.e., patented) to what purpose should anybody labour at it ?" To use a modern idiom, James Watt was not in business for his health.

The next attempt to solve the problem of mechanical traction was made by a Scotsman, William Symington, who designed a steam-coach in 1786. Ratchet drive was employed ; a model was exhibited at Edinburgh, but it seems unlikely that an actual carriage was built. The Earl of Caithness, who mentioned it in a paper to the British Association eighty years later said : " owing to the bad state of the roads, to speak in a slang way it was ' no go'." This might mean that a coach was built but failed, or that the state of the roads caused it not to be built.

More promise was shown by the three-cylinder tractor built two years later by Robert Fourness, of Elland (Halifax) ; but the inventor, who also worked at Otley and at Gainsborough, died young.

History records, too, the bare fact that in 1789 Thomas Allen, of London, designed a steam-carriage for passengers and goods.

§ 2 *Richard Trevithick* (1796-1803)

Richard Trevithick was born at Illogan, in Cornwall, and later resided hard by Murdock's house at Redruth. Watt lived nearby too, but Trevithick had no contact with him. Watt stated that Trevithick deserved hanging for inventing the high-pressure steam-engine : he held this view allegedly because he regarded high-pressure steam as dangerous : but no doubt the fact that his fortunes were tied up in low-pressure patents had some relevance. It seems that Trevithick was not on sociable terms with Murdock either : it is even reported that they fought a duel.

However, Trevithick no doubt heard of Murdock's experiments from his friend, Davies Gilbert ; in 1796 he built a three-wheeled model road-engine with a vertical cylinder, not unlike Murdock's, though he added a flywheel geared to the driving wheels to help it over dead-centre. Gilbert and Lady Dedunstanville of Tehidy encouraged him in his labours, and in 1801 in collaboration with his cousin Andrew Vivian he built a full-sized steam-carriage at Camborne, to which place he had moved. Subsequent history reasonably clear. Galloway, drawing on F. Trevithick's biography, says that this engine was burnt out on a trip to Tehidy ; that a second engine (1803) stuck in the road on a run to Redruth ; that the engine portion was sent to London and fitted with a new body, by Felton of Leather Lane; that it ran in public for some time at what is now Lord's Cricket Ground and also at Euston Square, and was finally broken up, the engine being sold to drive a hoop-mill.

These points are vouched for by documents, except the second. Probably only the first carriage ran in Cornwall though the engine of the second was built there. Some sources show the 1801 carriage as a horizontal-engined barouche, similar to that of 1803. Francis Trevithick* shows it as a vertical-engined machine, similar in many ways to the early model. Against this is the fact that a contemporary report in a Falmouth newspaper refers to it as " a carriage containing a small steam-engine," a description more fitted to the barouche. On the other hand, a passenger recalled that they were " very much squeezed together," and so while going up a hill several of them jumped off, a feat more easily effected from the platform of the vertical engine than from the high barouche. It appears that the castings of the 1801 engine were made at the Hayle foundry of Trevithick's father-in-law Harvey, and other parts at Coalbrookdale.

The second engine, fortunately, is described in a memorandum now at the Science Museum, written at the time by S. Goodrich. " Mr. T. has prepared an Engine for Driving a Coach Diameter of Cylinder 5½ Stroke 2ft. 6, 50 Strokes Per Minute work on each side Piston 20 lb. per inch in the boiler 30—about 110,000 lbs. 1 ft. high in a minute. The whole Engine, fire and all, is 6 cwt—the whole is

---

* " Life of Richard Trevithick."

contained within a cylinder boiler 2-9 long 2-6 Diameter." A rough sketch showing the boiler and a driving wheel was added.

Public reaction in London seems to have been one of alarm. When it ran down Tottenham Court Road the streets were cleared and shops closed. It must have been quite an alarming sight, with driving wheels some ten feet in diameter.

Trevithick's experiments with road carriages brought him no more success than his later ones with railway locomotives. But he had taken Murdock's idea far enough forward for the third Cornishman, Goldsworthy Gurney, to bring it to fruition. Gurney used to meet Davies Gilbert when he stayed with friends at St. Erth : so faith in the practicability of steam road locomotion was kept alive from 1786 until 1825.

One authority has stated that Trevithick also knew of the patents of Nathan Read, who had built a car* at Springfield, Massachusetts, in 1790. It is also recorded that Dr. Apollo Kinsley, of Hartford, Connecticut, drove a car at the end of the eighteenth century. This parallel development on both sides of the Atlantic is interesting ; but no hint as to whether interchange of ideas took place between the Old World and the New has been traced by the author.

One leaves the subject of the Cornish Giant with regret. Capt. Dick Trevithick was a genius, a fine man physically, and a generous friend. His life has been so fully described,† there can be no excuse for dilating on it here.

---

* Pinions on rear wheels driven by ratchets on the piston-rods ; exhaust steam turned aft to obtain reaction-propulsion.

† see H. W. Dickinson & A, Titley : " Richard Trevithick ; the Engineer & The Man," Cambridge, 1934.

§ 3 *Goldsworthy Gurney and Others* (1821-29)

During the sixteen years from 1805 to 1821 there is no record of a practical mechanical carriage being constructed in this country. Yet this was a period during which England was rapidly changing into an industrial nation, with ever-increasing demands for transport being met, as far as the roads themselves were concerned, by Telford and McAdam. The explanation is no doubt that the experiments of Trevithick and many colliery engineers with tramroad engines had made it clear that the future of heavy transport lay on the rails. When steam-carriage building began again it was of omnibuses and stage-coaches ; railways had not yet begun to cater for passenger traffic.

In 1821 Joseph Bramah had under construction in his Birmingham factory a steam stage-coach designed by Julius Griffiths of Brompton. It is usually shown with either a double barouche or an omnibus body, but later underwent a metamorphosis, for in Limberd's *Mirror* of 15 February 1823 it is described as a wagon weighing 3½ tons, capable of carrying three tons of goods. This is the only example of a vehicle being designed to carry goods during this period, and even this almost certainly never ran, although the chassis hung about in the factory for some years, and may have been out on trial trips. It appears that trouble was experienced with the water-tube boiler, the earliest-known example of this type. This machine, however, is important in that Walter Hancock saw the drawings of it and was partly influenced to enter road locomotion by them.

In 1823 Samuel Brown drove a carriage fitted with his patent " gas-vacuum " engine up Shooters Hill, near Woolwich. In this engine the partial vacuum obtained by combustion of carburetted hydrogen was applied to driving the pistons. Brown tried to form a company to operate his carriages. The *Mechanic's Chronicle* in 1824 reported : " . . . it is intended to raise only two thousand pounds, for the purpose of building one carriage, and no further sum shall be called for until a carriage shall have been propelled at the rate of 10 m.p.h. as far as York and back to London." Needless to say, this feat was not accomplished either then or at any time during the following seventy years.

In 1825 the great Goldsworthy Gurney first appeared on the road ; but before dealing with him there are some lesser lights to dispose of. James Neville, of Shad Thames, is reported to have constructed an engine in 1827, having springy metal plates attached to the wheel-rims to give easier riding. In the same year James Nasmyth, a young Edinburgh inventor, built an eight-seater steam-car at the request of the Scottish Society of Arts. He ran it a good deal on the Queensferry Road, and having demonstrated its practicability, broke it up, sold the boiler for £67, and turned to other matters. In 1827, too, the first fare-paying passengers were carried on a steam road vehicle. James Napier, one of the first generation of a line of outstanding engineers, conceived the idea of forging communications in the West of Scotland by means of steam-boats running in conjunction with steam-carriages. He built a road between Kilmuir and Loch Ech, putting upon it a steam-carriage of his own design. In his memoir he stated " I had a road made from Holy Loch to Loch Ech, on which I placed a steam-carriage,* thereby making a new route to Inverary and the Western Highlands. This steam-carriage was, I believe, the first that carried passengers for hire on common roads, being long before there were any railways in either England or Scotland carrying passengers by steam ; but

Sketch showing the design of carriage believed to have been built by Napier for his Holy Loch enterprise of 1827

from the softness and hilliness of the roads and more particularly from the want of knowledge how to make a boiler, we could not obtain the speed I expected." A contemporary report confirms " the roads were of no account at the time, and the motor was not a success."

Robert Napier, who was later associated with two other steam-carriage pioneers, Maudslay and Scott Russell, was joined with his brother James in this venture. These men could have started motoring on its way, had the purely mechanical side of the high-pressure steam-engine been better developed. Still active 20 years later, James offered to build an armoured fighting vehicle for use in the Crimean War, with a breech-loading gun " with an iron-proof casemate, mounted upon a steam-carriage." The idea was turned down by the War Office " without assigning any reason." Although Lord Roberts used a Fowler armoured road train in South Africa, it needed sixty years more of sweat and tears before the A.F.V. was accepted. Even then it was developed by the Royal Navy and not the Army.

Goldsworthy Gurney was the first designer really to achieve success, perhaps because he paid attention first to developing a suitable boiler. Gurney was born at Treator, near Padstow, in 1793, and he passed the first 27 years of his life there. During school holidays he used to stay with friends at St. Erth. It is thought that he was introduced to Trevithick by D. Gilbert (see P. 7) and

---

* A patent published by him in 1831 showed a four-wheeled drag with horizontal boiler, two cylinders at the side driving a counter-shaft in front on the front axle : final drive by chain.

that he had an opportunity of seeing some of the steam-carriage trials at Camborne. If this is so, on arrival in London in 1820 he would already have been convinced of the practicability of steam road locomotion. Dr. Dionysius Lardner, however, says that Gurney was appointed lecturer in chemistry at the Surrey Institution, and as a result of experiments on heat his attention was directed to the question of carriages. In 1823 he projected a vehicle driven by ammonia gas ; in 1825 he drove his first steam carriage up Windmill Hill at Enfield.

Gurney's boiler was of an interesting type. It consisted of a layer of tubes shaped like a letter V on its side, the ends running into two horizontal boilers connected by two vertical tubes. The steam passed out of the top boiler in a steam-chest, and thence through the smoke-box to the cock, the primed water returning to the lower boiler. The exhaust steam was passed to a receptacle called a blowing-box, which received the steam in a series of puffs and let it issue through jets in a continuous stream. The feed-water was heated by being passed through tubes coiled inside the blowing-box.

Gurney was convinced, as were many others, that a smooth wheel could not obtain sufficient adhesion on the road. He therefore arranged his wheels to carry the weight only, propulsion being by iron " legs " digging into the surface of the road, repeatedly thrust to the rear and retracted by the action of the pistons.

His second carriage in 1826 fitted pushers for use in emergency only, and in further ones they were omitted altogether. (The same underestimate of the gripping power of a smooth wheel was made by the railway engineers, leading to costly schemes of cog-and-ratchet and chain propulsion.) This second vehicle seated six passengers inside and fifteen outside, and is said to have weighed only 1½ tons. An extra pair of wheels was fitted in front of the fore-carriage, and these were steered, thus bringing round the fore-carriage and the coach itself. Gurney drove this coach up Brockley and Stanmore hills without needing to use the legs. He apparently feared the twisting strain imposed on a normal wheel by being driven from the centre, and he transmitted the drive from the axle to the wheel-rim by using carrier bars, just as Thornycroft did 80 years later.

Gurney was now making quite long journeys. He ran from London to Melksham and back ; he had intended going on to Bath, but he was attacked and injured by a mob at a Fair at Melksham. One report says that the carriage was taken on to Bath by horses, to prevent any more anti-machinery rioting. But Young says that Bailey, the principal engineer, was taken on a horse-stage to Bath " in an insensible state " ; if true it implies that the steamer did not go to Bath, even behind horses. The return journey of 84 miles was run in 9½ hours, burning 48 bushels of coke. It has been stated that this coach later ran on a South Wales railway. Certainly Wm. Crawshay, Jnr., of the Cyfarthfa ironworks purchased a Gurney engine in 1830, for the Hirwain Plateway ; but although he refers to it as a carriage it was more likely one of the 1829-type drags. Crawshay made a number of traction experiments, but because the figures he and Gurney give for the tare weight of the engine continually differ, one cannot be sure whether its performance was creditable or not. Hebert was of the opinion that it consumed many times as much coke for the same work as other railway locomotives. It is believed that a second Gurney engine also went to work on the Plateway.

There was at this time a great public fear of boiler-bursts, not entirely unfounded. This influenced Gurney to design a " drag," in which the engine portion was distinct from the carriage, and of course detachable. This was tested at Hounslow Barracks in 1829, in the presence of the Duke of Wellington, who said " they are of great national importance " and " it is scarcely possible to calculate the benefit we shall derive from such an invention."

This machine had many interesting features. One was the provision of " shoe-drags," which were flat feet on strong spindles passing up through hollow cylinders, which could be used to provide braking by pressing on the road, or to raise the wheels off the ground. (Let modern motor advertisers who sing of built-in jacks doff their hats !) *The Mirror* of 26 September 1829, quoting Herapath for these details, adds : " On the right hand of the director lies the handle of the throttle-valve, by which he has the power of increasing or diminishing the supply of steam *ad libitum*, and hence accelerating or retarding the carriage's velocity. The whole carriage and machinery weighs 16 cwt., and with full complement of water and coke, 20 or 22 cwts . . ."

Herapath rode with Gurney during the Hounslow tests. " At eighteen minutes after three I ascended the carriage with Mr. Gurney. ' Now,' said Mr. Gurney ' I will show you her speed.' He did, and we completed seven turns round the outside of the road by twenty-eight minutes after three . . . nearly 17 miles per hour." A " Man of Science," writing of the drags in the *Atlas*, suggested " if ultimately found capable of public use, locomotive engines should be exchanged . . . at certain stages for the purpose of tightening of screws and other adjustments . . ." This is a reminder that the lack of accurate tools at this time rendered good workmanship extremely difficult. It was with similar machines that Sir Charles Dance operated his Gloucester-Cheltenham service of four trips daily each way, running 9 miles in 45-60 minutes. Between February 27 and June 22 (1831) the company ran 4,000 operational miles. On June 23 an axle broke, bringing public mistrust to a head and leading to the suspension of the regular service.

Wherever Dance's carriages ran he was met with severe counter-measures by persons interested in their failure. Heaps of stones were put down upon the turnpike roads where the steamers were running. Writing of one of these occasions, Dance's chief engineer, Mr. Stone, reported that the steamer got through twice, but broke an axle on the third trip. Horsed coaches were stopped by the stones : "The *Champion*, from London, a fine four-horse coach, was brought up, and in whipping to get through broke the harness to pieces."

The turnpike charges were racked up against steam vehicles, and although a Select Committee of the House of Commons advised that this practice should be stopped, nothing was done.

It is only fair to add that Sir Frederick Bramall, an acute observer (whose first job as an apprentice was breaking up a Gurney boiler with a cold chisel), thought that public lack of interest rather than stones and toll-charges brought about the steam-stage's downfall. The common road steam-carriage could run at only 15 m.p.h. against the rail's sixty, and public allegiance was definitely on the latter's side.

The road people lacked showmanship, too. When Gurney took a carriage to Glasgow, the *Glasgow Chronicle* commented " . . . instead of coming by road through some great English towns, he brought it by smack to Leith, and when he tried to travel from Edinburgh to Glasgow he required horses to help him up the hills." If the carriage-builders had waited until their teething troubles were over, and then gone out with flags flying and bugles blowing, the people might have been won over. As it was, most of them carried out their unsuccessful trials too publicly and ran their long trips too quietly.

Gurney realised that a lot more money must be spent before the carriages became really workable, and he petitioned Parliament for a grant to enable him to carry on the work. A Select Committee recommended a grant of £16,000, but the Treasury refused to pay it. Looking back, this seems to be the decision that sealed road trans-port's fate for sixty years to come. At that time railways hardly existed, and the road had a chance : by the mid-thirties it was too late. Gurney felt himself badly treated and passed to other scientific activity, for which he was knighted.

The *Mechanic's Magazine* said of Gurney : " Never was there a person who had less claim on the National purse. He has left steam locomotion where he found it." Unless the writer knew of more workable pre-Gurney carriages than we do now, the verdict must be dubbed uncharitable. In some ways, however, Dance did more than Gurney to make road motors a sound proposition. That he had some trouble with Gurney's vehicles is certain. Col. Macerone, who of course was far from disinterested, stated in *A Few Facts* " . . . such is the frequency of derangements, especially the bursting of one or more tubes in the boiler, that it required the utmost exertions of an engineer (Mr. Stone) at a salary of £1 per day, and four men at £3 per week, to keep one of the three coaches in moving order." It is known that all the drags were painted exactly alike, so that the public could not tell how frequently they had to be changed.

In 1833 Sir Charles Dance had a more powerful boiler put in one of the drags by Messrs. Maudslay & Field. He seems to have got quite good results, for he drove from London to Brighton, towing a 15-seat omnibus, in 5½ hours : the return journey was made in less than five hours. The party left Maudslay Sons and Field's factory in Lambeth at 8-18 on 20 September 1833. They reached Croydon in 47 minutes, Merstham in 1 hour 54 minutes, Crawley in 3 hours 1 minute, and then stopped at Peas Pottage Gate for coke and water. The passenger list comprised Sir Charles, Mr. Field, Mr. J. Maudslay, Mr. Alexander Gordon, " three other engineers and five gentlemen."

For a fortnight this combination ran in service from Wellington Street, over Waterloo Bridge, to Greenwich. Sir Frederick Bramall tells of a journey behind this drag from Hyde Park Corner to Reading, towing a full omnibus. Both driving wheels were keyed to the axle, and " the right-angle turn into the inn yard (at Reading) was not made without a succession of backings and fillings, and my impression is that even with these we did not accomplish it without sacrificing one of the gateposts."

On the return trip the stoker was tired " although he had had a good dinner " and let the firebars become clinkered. Progress became slow : most of the passengers got tired of sitting in the 'bus, and " we arrived at Hyde Park Corner at the height of the ' season ' sitting on the roof and covered in blacks." This drag ran for many years.

Meanwhile there were other inventors interesting themselves in road transport. David Gordon, who had made some experiments on compressed-air carriages with Murdock in 1819, built a steam-'bus in 1824, driven by rods thrusting on the road. Sir James Anderson and W. H. James took out patents in 1824 for a carriage having two boilers and four 3½ in. cylinders in two pairs. A carriage built under these patents ran a trial trip in Epping Forest in 1829, with fifteen passengers on board. One of the boilers (which comprised a number of water-tubes) failed, but the vehicle got home on the steam from the other. It was dismantled, and the inventors set about improving the design, using a boiler in which some 400 feet of ¾-inch tube was enclosed in a space 4 ft. by 3 ft. by 2 ft. Luke Hebert, who assisted at the trials of this new vehicle, stated that it was not much of a success. There is an engraving in Fletcher of a James carriage, dated 1830, an eighteen-seat mail-coach of orthodox design. No contemporary writer seems to have heard of it, and examination of the coloured print from which it was taken shows that it was published in 1828 by a Mr. Adcock, and purports only to show what the James coach would look like when completed.

Another pair of inventors, Messrs. Burstall & Hill, of Leith (who were unsuccessful entrants in the Rainhill Locomotive Trials of 1829) built a carriage about 1824 ; the boiler was carried on a two-wheel trailer at the rear, with flexible steam connections. A medallion was struck at the time bearing a representation of this coach; but all E. A. Cowper could say of it at the Institution of Mechanical Engineers in 1879 was : " Burstall's engine was tried at Deptford, where it burst." The same inventors' new carriage of 1825, which dispensed with the boiler-trailer, was intended for running on either road or rail : it was replete with ill-digested good ideas including optional four-wheel drive, exhaust-silencer and power-driven fuel-pump. As a prime-mover it was disappointing, only reaching 4 m.p.h.

A vehicle of 1828 that was decidedly before its time was the steam-lorry built by the Frenchman, Onesyme Pecqueur, with

Incomplete details of Pecqueur's steam-wagon of 1828. From contemporary French sources

epicyclic gearbox and differential on the rear axle. The boiler was in front of the driver, the engine under his seat, and drive to the rear axle by a long chain. It differed hardly at all from the machines which became popular in England after 1900.

A man called Fraser seems to have built two vehicles in or after 1829. Of the first nothing is known ; the second had four cylinders $2\frac{1}{4}$ by 9 in., and incorporated a body with a low loading line similar to James' second carriage. The *Mechanic's Magazine* of November 14th, 1829, records that it " . . . proceeded from Vauxhall Bridge to the Swan Inn at Clapham, a distance of $2\frac{1}{2}$ miles, which was run at the rate of 15 m.p.h."

So ended the eighteen-twenties. Some twenty steam carriages had been built, and development was proceeding apace ; the road had secured a lead, for no passengers had yet been regularly hauled by steam-power on a railway.

§ 4 *The Steam-Carriages' Heyday* (1831-1838)

The name of Walter Hancock dominates common road loco-motives in the eighteen-thirties. Because he was the least commer-cially unsuccessful his name has lived on in popular accounts where many of his contemporaries' have not. Even at the time he was most often featured in the newspapers and magazines.

According to Rhys Jenkins he first became interested in road locomotion because it seemed a good field for a small engine he had designed, using an expanding bag in place of a cylinder. The engine was a failure, but he kept on in the steam-carriage business, using first oscillating cylinders and then the orthodox type. In his first vehicle of 1828 the two oscillating cylinders drove the single front wheel ; in his second, the *Infant I,* of 1830, they drove the rear axle by pitch-chain. In the *Infant II* (1831) vertical fixed cylinders were employed, but chain-drive was retained and employed in all his vehicles.

In 1832 came the larger *Era, Enterprise* (first called *Demonstration*), and possibly the *Sun,* though this does not appear in Hancock's own account, and it may be apocryphal. In 1833 came the *Autopsy,* and in 1834 a second *Era,* renamed *Erin* when it made a visit to Dublin under the auspices of the Hibernian Steam Carriage Com-pany. In 1834 Hancock built a drag for a Mr. Voigtlander of Vienna, which made a trip under test on a route through Bow back to the City Road via Homerton, Clapton, Tottenham and Crouch End, with nine persons on the drag and a six-seater carriage in tow. He also built a drag for a customer in Ireland about this time.

The name *Autopsy* means " see for yourself." Baudry de Saunier wrote " . . . it is a queer way to encourage people to try a new method of transport, which invokes the image of the operation which they might be unfortunate enough to suffer." In Hancock's own list he interpolates here a three-seater gig, and it seems probable that this car, often referred to as his last, was in fact built in early 1835, and that in 1838 a further six-seater car was built, on much the same lines (see Plate VI). In 1835 the last omnibus, the *Automaton,* was built, being a return to the earlier open-sided style.

All Hancock's buses carried a crew of three : the driver, the engineer in the engine-room to look after and oil the engines, and a lad at the rear to keep the fire fed with coke, which was carried in a bunker on the back platform. The seating capacity of the buses and cars was as follows :—

	Out-side	In-side				Out-side	In-side
First car	4			Erin	...	6	8
Infant I	10			*Autopsy*	...	5	9
Infant II	14			Gig	...	3	
Era	2	16		*Automaton*	...		22
Enterprise		14		Last car	...	6	

Dimensions cannot be given : there is a scale drawing in Lavergne's book, but as this shows a height inside the body of only 3½ feet it is suspect.

The circumstances under which Hancock's carriages ran in public service have been often repeated, and there is no need to detail them here. From 1831 until 1836 the carriages as they came into service were employed running between the Bank and Stratford, Paddington, Islington and Pentonville. Not continuously, however. The *Mechanic's Magazine* of August 10th, 1833, stated : " Steam travelling since the disappearance of Mr. Hancock from the road, at the end of his late brilliant career, has been at a standstill." This valediction was premature. For five months in 1836 the *Infant II*, *Era*, *Enterprise* and *Autopsy* were running together on the Paddington Road. The failure of the operating companies, rather than failure of the carriages, prevented the expected expansion. Hancock was one of the few builders who began by perfecting a really serviceable boiler, and he seems to have been singularly free from the boiler trouble that beset his rivals.

Besides having left an autobiography, Hancock was well served by the press of the time, and there is plenty of material concerning him available. There is space here for only a few items.

One of his first long trips was in *Infant II*, to Brighton, in October, 1832 ; the thirteen passengers included Alexander Gordon, a naval officer, and a scientist. The car ran over Blackfriars Bridge at 9 m.p.h., and up Redhill at 6 m.p.h., but Hancock wrote that shortage of coke and water spoiled the trip : " We had to pump water at all the streams we came across."

A cutting from the *Morning Herald* of 25/10/36 is of interest in showing how London had accepted the presence of Hancock's machines : " As Mr. Hancock's steam-carriage *Autopsy* was proceeding as usual yesterday morning to Paddington, a little beyond the Regent's Park, the carriage was in a moment brought to a dead stand. As no derangement could be discovered in any of the exposed parts of the machinery, and as most of the passengers had before been put down, he decided upon making no further examination on the road ; but as he wished to try the power of his last new carriage, the *Era*, he determined on taking the *Autopsy* in tow of the *Era* back to the station on the City Road. The latter was soon on the spot, the former attached to it, and the carriages moved off in company ; but the ascent of Pentonville Hill (nearly ½ mile long and rising one in twenty at the steepest part) was the point of great interest ; however, the hill was ascended half-way with ease, when the slow motion was put on, and the two carriages cleared it without any further stoppage." Later it was found the key in one of *Autopsy's* slide-valves had shaken out.

The *Automaton*, just before its completion, was converted into a drag and hauled three omnibuses and a stage-coach, containing in all 50 passengers, at 10-14 m.p.h. up Whitehall to Charing Cross, then up Regent Street and Oxford Street to Shepherd's Bush and Brentford. It also made a trip to Marlborough.

Sir Frederick Bramall recalled in *The Engineer* of August 17th, 1894, that when he was an apprentice in London, Hancock used to take an interest in him, and let him ride down on the carriage at the end of the day to his factory at Stratford. Bramall's boss was a man called Hague, father-in-law to Summers, the steam-carriage designer, and no doubt Hancock and young Bramall would have much to talk about concerning the then small world of engineering. Bramall never told what they spoke about as the carriage steamed along the leafy lanes out to Stratford ; but he recalled to a meeting of the Institution of Civil Engineers some forty years later that Hancock had told him " You may be surprised to hear that the point in which I found most trouble is one that seems the most simple : the tyres of the driving wheels, owing to their great wear."

Hancock was not free of the contemporary wordy warfare. In the preface to his autobiography he writes : " At the moment of going to press, the writer has been informed that there are persons making attempts to improve both railway and road steamers by adopting colorable imitations of his patents . . . whatever improvements may result from the mode of generating steam by means of flat chambers, exposing large thin sheets of water to the action of corresponding thin volumes of heated air through flues formed of alternate chambers placed side by side—the writer claims this as the grand and principal feature of his invention : and should tortuous or colorable imitations to deprive him of the results of his continued and expensive exertions be attempted, he confidently hopes that the support of the public will in vain be sought in behalf of the authors of such proceedings."

The London & Greenwich Company's engineer, D. Redmund, had ordered the *Enterprise* from Hancock, and upon taking delivery began building his *Alpha*, copying the former in every detail except the wheels. Redmund's had hollow cast-iron spokes, and he seems to have employed the differential steering system of the front wheels patented by Ackerman in 1816 (not used again until 1872 by Bollée). This vehicle ran private trials, but seems not to have gone into service.

The *Mechanic's Magazine* of August 31, 1833, published " an imaginary conversation in Peterborough Court " between several experts, " Professor Crackwell," " Dick Dubious," " Sir Dionysius Dawlucker," and others, in which it was stated that Redmund's carriage had been filled with foul water and had primed outside the Yorkshire Stingo. On this somewhat insecure foundation Redmund threatened the Editor with a Court action.

Hancock had little real competition. Sir Charles Dance's Field-Maudslay drag appeared briefly on the Wellington Street-Greenwich route, but neither Col. Macerone at Paddington Wharf nor Capt. Nathaniel Ogle and William Alltoft Summers in Cable

Street seem to have been interested in the city routes. Yates & Smith were close at hand, in Whitechapel, but their carriages appear to have run very little. The General Steam Carriage Company, of Moorgate, ran on some of Hancock's routes, but did not start until 1841, when the latter was off the road. It is quite true that at the close of Hancock's career challenges came rumbling over the Irish Sea from Sir James Anderson's workshops at Buttevant Castle, but nothing but verbiage resulted. No : Hancock was undoubtedly master of the field ; but he could not go forward against the bad faith of his associates and the public lack of interest, due to the expanding empire of the rail.

In October, 1839, he began running the *Automaton* on the London to Cambridge route, covering the 52 miles from the Four Swans in Bishopsgate in 4½ hours. There were scenes of enthusiasm ; at Cambridge about 40 people scrambled aboard, and Hancock found the carriage too heavy to steer : he ran into a ditch and broke some spokes. In July, 1840, the *Automaton* was hired by the Stratford Cricket Club to carry their eleven and 21 spectators to a game in Epping Forest.

Finally, a few details of Hancock's contemporaries. Messrs. W. & G. & R. Heaton, of Birmingham, were running a vertical-cylindered steam drag, with a rather complex transmission system, about 1833, and on a trip from Worcester to Birmingham, hauling a coach carrying 20 passengers it " proceeded to ascend the Lickey Hill, a rise of 1 in 9, and even 1 in 8 in some places ; many parts of the hill were very soft, but by putting both wheels in gear they ascended to the summit, 700 yards in 9 minutes."

In 1833 a company was formed in Birmingham to construct and operate a Heaton carriage, subject to its keeping up an average of 10 m.p.h. After repeated trials, the Heaton Brothers dissolved the contract, candidly declaring their inability to do more than 7 or 8 m.p.h. (This is the version of Macerone ; another authority states 15 m.p.h. was asked for and only 12 obtained). A statement by the Company in the *Birmingham Journal* of April 12th, 1834, said " . . . wear and tear were excessive at 10 m.p.h." The carriage* was built in the Heaton factory in Shadwell Street.

Ogle and Summers, already mentioned, are chiefly known because they deposed before the Select Committee of 1834 that their carriages had run continuously at over 30 m.p.h. They first built a three-wheeled triple Phaeton† in 1830, operated from their station in Cable Street, London. It ran to within 2½ miles of Basingstoke, where the crank-axle broke. It was sent back to London by barge.

* Two vertical cylinders 7 by 12 in. ; variable speed gears. (Plate IV.)

† 5 ft. 6 in. driving wheel, two 7½ by 18 in. cyls., verticle water-tube boiler, 250 sq. ft. heating surface.

During 1931 they seem to have been building another carriage* at Southampton. This ventured out in January, 1832, on the Winchester road, but by the time it reached Compton steam was roaring through the safety-valve and it was judged unwise to proceed any further. The *Hants Chronicle*, however, stated that it " actually came at the rate of 26 miles an hour, in spite of slippery roads."

It would appear that this vehicle later ran a considerable mileage, and the reason why it has always been assumed that this pair were not successful is not clear. No doubt they did not travel so fast or so far as they claimed, but their achievements were not inconsiderable. A breathless reporter from the *Saturday Magazine* told in the issue of October 6th, 1832, how " I have just returned from witnessing the triumph of science in mechanics, travelling along a hilly and crowded road from Oxford to Birmingham in a steamcarriage. This truly wonderful machine is the invention of Capt. Ogle of the Royal Navy, and Mr. Summers his partner, and is the first and only one that has accomplished so long a journey over chance roads, and without rails . . . Just as the steam-carriage was entering the town of Birmingham, the supply of coke became exhausted, the steam dropped, and the good people, on learning the cause, flew to the frame and dragged it into the stable yard."

Dr. Church was the designer of at least one ornate steam diligence, often depicted in full steam on the open road, plastered over with laurel leaves, armorial ensignia and decorative moulding. He built at Bramah's Yard, between 1832 and 1835, and though the Birmingham Gazette called attention to "Church's beautiful engine running on the Coventry road, six miles out and six miles back, on heavy roads," his engines (which may have been the same one progressively rebuilt), seem always to have failed. He issued several prospectuses that were never implemented, and then went to America. One witness in the Doctor's favour must be quoted. Mr. F. W. Turner, in 1860, found in a Swansea ironworks, and put into running order, a small railway engine that Church had built for the London & Birmingham Railway in 1838, called *Eclipse*. It was, he said " very ingenious and well-constructed."

Yet another Birmingham inventor was G. Millichap, credited with the construction of a carriage in 1834. His patent was for a vehicle running on six wheels, the rear-most pair being very close together ; but whether one was so built is uncertain.

It is now a pleasure to turn to the career of Lt./Col. Francis Macerone. No writer, whether of Gilbertian farces or Shakespearian tragedy, could wish for a more sympathetic subject. By claiming that the Spanish Ambassador had laid a plot to kidnap him aboard a Spanish frigate lying at the Nore, a beautiful lady being the bait, Macerone exhibits the comic-opera side of his character. By his

* Weight 3 tons, 3 cyls. 4 by 12 in., driving axle direct. Boiler on separate carriage in original design.

PLATE 1

N. J. Cugnot's steam-wagon of 1771, as now preserved in the Conservatoire des Arts et Métiers in Paris

The probable appearance of Trevithick's Camborne vehicle of 1801. (From a drawing prepared from hearsay by F. Trevithick).

The probable appearance of the first British road motor, built by Fourness in 1788. From early mechanical details

Trevithick's 1803 carriage: from Galloway's "The Steam Engine" published in 1881

PLATE II

Left : Julius Griffiths' coach of 1821, from contemporary drawings. Right : incomplete details of coach constructed according to W. H. James' 1824 patents

Top, left : James Fraser's coach of 1829 ; right : Gordon's " pusher " omnibus of 1824. Bottom, left : Burstall & Hill's carriage of 1825, and (right) the same inventors' coach of 1824, with boiler on a separate carriage. All these are from early prints

Left : a Gurney Cheltenham drag of 1830, as given by Gordon Right : the James drag of 1829 : after Hebert

PLATE III

" Mr. Gurney's new steam-carriage as it appeared in the Regent's Park on Thursday December 6." From " The Observer " of 9 December 1827

GURNEY'S IMPROVED STEAM CARRIAGE.

From " The Mirror " of 26 September, 1829. This purports to show the drag which was demonstrated at Hounslow Barracks before the Duke of Wellington.

PLATE IV

*James Nasmyth's motor-car of 1827.
From an illustration published in his
biography*

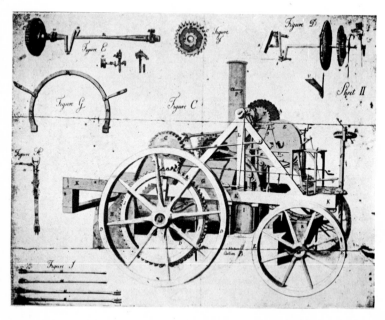

*Working drawings of the Heaton Brothers' drag of 1832 ; by
courtesy of Birmingham Central Library*

remark that " at every side I was faced by the Remora of Destitution"
he shows that he sometimes wore the tragic mask.

Alexander Gordon wrote: " accustomed as *aide-de-camp* to
Murat, King of Naples, to follow that dauntless cavalry officer,
Col. Macerone still retains his love of quick motion." In becoming a
steam-carriage builder the Colonel chose the hard way to attaining
quick motion, although when his creditors were about he had a
fair turn of speed on his feet.

It was in 1831 that he joined his associate, John Squire; " I was
without much money, having through the fortunes of war returned
from Turkey with even less than I went out with. Mr. F. C. Parry,
a lawyer, provided funds for establishing a factory at Paddington
Wharf. I placed Mr. Squire in a house on the premises as foreman."

Together they built an eleven-seater steam-carriage before 1832,
and a seventeen-seater* in the following year. Funds were very
low, the Colonel recorded : " the journey to Windsor was effected
with the produce of my last watch," and later " . . . I had not
the wherewithal to buy a sack of coke." A wealthy gentleman
loaned him £100, but when this was not returned in full " the kind
Christian man hunted me down like a felon, and has done ever since,
for the balance." In 1834 Macerone quarrelled with Squire, and
they parted.

Both the carriages had been sent abroad, one to Brussels and the
other to Paris. The *Journal de Paris* thought the coach excellent,
" and by no means so noisy as that of M. Dietz." A Jew called
Azada handled the matter, sold the patent rights and pocketed the
cash : Macerone got nothing. At least one of the carriages never
returned to this country.

Macerone was sensitive to criticism. In those days no punches
were pulled in the alleys behind Fleet Street. Here is an incident
that reveals his fear of the press. Macerone had arranged a trip to
Birmingham, and a Mr. McNeill agreed to provide stations of coke
along the route. Just before the trip was to take place, McNeill
wrote to Macerone that he had had no reply from the innkeepers
he had asked to supply the coke, but supposed it would be in readiness.
The Colonel refused to start unless the coke was ensured. " Had I
stopped for want of coke, what would have been the cry or yell
of the writers in the *Mechanic's Magazine*, and others of my inveterate
persecutors ! There is, in particular, one skulking anonymous
slanderer who signs himself ' H.' I called upon the insolent poltroon
to show his face ; but he has not done so."

Gurney had a dispute with Macerone and tried to get him
arrested. " I was not actually taken," wrote the Colonel blandly,
" because I turned the tables on the officers, and confined them on
the premises, while I walked away." He had locked them in his

* Vertical water-tube boiler 150 lb., two 7½ by 15¾ in. cyls.

The *Mechanic's Magazine* stated in 1833 that one of Macerone's carriages
had run for five years, but this cannot be confirmed.

office : apparently they hung around for several weeks waiting for the gentleman to return, but he had gone abroad, deeming it wise, in spite of the inconvenience, to give Paddington Wharf a wide berth. The concluding stages of this character's career are dealt with in the next section.

Meanwhile, many other inventors were trying their hand at road locomotion. Wm. Mann, of Brixton, had built a compressed-air driven carriage in 1830. Richard Roberts (of Sharp, Roberts, of Manchester), built an engine in 1833 (apparently a drag of some sort) and in 1834 ran a trip from his factory in Falkner Street, 1½ miles up Oxford Road, at 20 m.p.h. Later the same year this engine burst a boiler tube, and the explosion scattered the fire and broke a shop window. As usual, local reporters seized upon the opportunity of painting a picture of terrible carnage.

Still further north, John Scott Russell built six coaches* at the Grove House Engine Works in Edinburgh. Two of these were running in London in 1833, to Windsor, Greenwich and Kew. He established an hourly service between Glasgow and Paisley, running the 7 miles in 34 minutes. The carriages each hauled a tender or curricle to supply coke and water *en route*, as well as an omnibus. Spare tenders were kept along the route ; passengers were carried upon these tenders at a cheap rate. This service began in April, 1834.

Russell encountered the usual opposition, but with their large cylinders the carriages were able to plough through heaps of stones of almost any depth. On one occasion, however, a wheel was broken, and the strain on the frame weakened the boiler, which burst at Halfway House, killing three and injuring others. This brought the service to a close, but the carriages continued to run at various places ; A. R. Sennett stated that they were running from Glasgow in 1846, and they were still going as late as 1857 according to Lavergne.

One figure that deserves mention, although not a steam-carriage builder, is Alexander Gordon. He travelled on almost every steam-carriage of the time, and left some valuable written work. He gave evidence before the Select Committee of 1834. A year earlier he had called " A Meeting of Noblemen and Gentlemen . . . at Fendall's Hotel, Palace Yard, for the purpose of forming a Society for Ameliorating the Distress of the Country by means of Steam Transport and Agriculture." Dance and Hancock were among those present, but nothing useful was done.

Mention of Gordon brings up the matter of contemporary lists of steam-carriage builders, which provide evidence that there were a few carriages built at this time about which we do not know anything.

One list was drawn up by Macerone in 1834 ; he mentions all the well-known builders before that date, and concludes with a list

* Two vertical cylinders 12 by 12 in.

of inventors whose carriages " would not move at all." These are :
Mr. Boaze, Mr. Gibbs, Mr. Joyce, Dr. Harland, Mr. Holland, Dr.
Church, Mr. Fraser, Mr. Rich. Macerone may have been a little
too harsh in this. He was never charitable towards fellow-inventors.
Church and Fraser have already been dealt with. Gibbs had travelled
100 miles in Dance's carriages to gain experience, and together with a
Mr. Chaplin he had designed or built in 1830 a tractor of some sort
having friction-band clutches on the rear wheels to facilitate
cornering. With a Mr. Applegarth, he built a drag in 1832, and
perhaps a carriage as well. Dr. Harland, of Scarborough, tried a
condensing engine, but it probably never ran.

Another list is Alexander Gordon's showing carriages built or
building in 1833 ; this was republished by Young, with a few
additions, and showed 19 vehicles in all : Hancock 5, Gurney-
Stone-Gibbs-Maudslay 1, Ogle 1, Squire 1, Fraser 1, Palmer 1
(at Bramah's), Gibbs-Applegarth 1 ; building : Gatfield & Bower
1, Andrew Smith 1, Redmund 1, Manton 1, Phillips 1, Silk 1,
Smith & Co. 1, an anonymous inventor in East London 1.

In 1834 the journal *Arcana of Science*, which Young had apparently
not seen, also published a list, differing from Gordon's in that it
credits Gibbs with a drag and a carriage, ignores Phillips, and in
place of the Gurney-Stone-Gibbs-Maudsley one includes Maudslay
1, Gurney 4, Dance 3, Field 1.

Manton (who is called Manting in the *Arcana*) may have been
J. Manton, of Messrs. Manton, the gunsmiths. The Palmer mentioned is presumably G. H. Palmer, of Grays Inn Road, a prolific

*Incomplete details of one of the Summers & Ogle coaches (left)
and the Gibbs drag of 1832 (right)*

inventor. Andrew Smith may be one half of the Yates & Smith
partnership, which built a carriage in Whitechapel ; but the first
trip of this vehicle (along Leman Street and High Street) is supposed
to have been on 1 July 1834, after Gordon's list was closed. For
the rest, the dust of years has settled over their wheeltracks.

It is curious that Maudslay and Field are both credited with a
carriage by the *Arcana*. As a matter of fact, this pair were at pains
to disown any interest in carriages when they gave evidence before
the Select Committee. When asked if there was a carriage called

" The Field & Maudslay carriage," they hastened to say it had been built " for some gentlemen " and they were not the owners. Asked if it was a success, they stated only that it had run many trips the previous summer. The evidence at this enquiry makes interesting reading : there is not space to give it here, but it was fully reported in the *Mechanic's Magazine*. One fact that emerged was that Hancock did not know the horse-power of his carriages, though he thought the *Autopsy* was eight. There ensued a discussion as to whether this was equivalent to having eight horses in the shafts.

Returning for a moment to the *Arcana* list, it will be noted that Gurney, Dance, Field and Maudslay, who were known to be associated in some degree, are credited with 9 carriages between them. If the 3 Gloucester-Cheltenham drags are credited to Dance, the Field-boilered drag of 1833 to Field, that leaves Maudslay's unaccounted for, and also implies that Gurney, besides his two carriages and a drag of 1825-6-8, must have built another vehicle. There are many conflicting engravings of Gurney drags, but few of them are worth anything as evidence.

Finally, a salute to inventors of the 'thirties across the Channel, notably Charles Dietz of Paris, whose drags were hauling omnibuses and goods ; and across the Atlantic, where Harrison Dyer of Boston, Joseph Dixon of Lynn, near Boston, Rufus Porter of Hartford, Connecticut, and James of New York, had all been briefly on the road.

§ 5 *The Decline in Steam-Coaching* (1839-57)

To return to the metaphor with which this survey opened, the first few pages of mechanical transport history have now been turned. Now, as the Victorian way of life gathers force, chapter after chapter is rapidly written. But almost all of it tells of railway projection and construction, of the Stephensons' six-wheeled engines which were now rushing along the iron tracks at speeds up to sixty miles per hour. The railway was beginning its sixty years of undisputed rule. As early as 1839 someone was asking in the columns of the *Mechanic and Chemist* : " are the working classes of the country to suffer want and starvation because the London & Birmingham Railway are to monopolise all the traffic of the manufacturing districts ? " For all that, interest in automobile construction was kept alive, now and again burning up brightly, only to be snuffed almost to extinction by restrictive legislation.

In 1838 there were more than a dozen carriages still running : Scott Russell's six, three or four of Hancock's, at least one of Macerone, at least one Gurney drag and probably Dance's as well. Several people were still building. But the press had lost interest in road carriages now that railways were opening up all over the country, and it is difficult to find any record of their activities.

We know, however, that on 20 July 1840 Mr. J. T. Beale, of East Greenwich, drove a Macerone coach, which he had built, up Shooters Hill, Eltham, at 14 m.p.h. " and was blowing off at the top " ; and that three days later " Macerone's new coach ran from Deptford to Bromley in 28 minutes." Unfortunately, Beale had a dispute with the General Steam Carriage Co., who had ordered the carriage, over the price. Macerone suffered indirectly from this, and was sold up by the bailiffs. He was now destitute, and in the *Mechanic's Magazine* of 13 November 1841 he advertised his boiler-patents for sale, claiming that his carriage had run every day for eighteen months at 12-20 m.p.h., without repair. He was taken up on this by a reader, and in reply agreed that the expression " every day " should be taken " *cum grano salis*." " We have 52 Lord's days in the year," he explained, " which are not common road steam days." He also stated that his friend Squire " being of an obstinate temperament," would not learn the correct way to forge cranks, with the result that they sometimes gave way. He further referred to the dispute with Beale over the price of the carriage, and stated " at every step I am met by the Remora of Destitution."

This incident seems to show that he and Squire had come together again. The *Mechanic's Magazine* in August 1841 announced : " The steam locomotionists are again on the road . . . the General Steam Carriage Co. have been making daily trips from the York & Albany Hotel, Regent's Park, to the Manor House at Tottenham, using Mr. Squire's Steam Carriage." This may have been Macerone's new coach ; Squire took out patents for a boiler for steam-carriages in 1843 (apostrophised by Macerone as an infringement of his patents), but there is no evidence to prove that he built a coach of his own design. An illustration of Squire's *Albert* carriage of 1843 shows a vehicle very similar to the Macerone design. (Plate VIII).

This is the last we hear of Macerone in connection with road locomotion. But his dynamic, if superficial, energy seems to have found other outlets; in 1842 he was writing in the *Mechanic's Magazine* on many subjects, including atmospheric railways, marine kites, wood-paving, filtration and lightning conductors.

An apparently successful inventor who has received little attention is F. Hills, of the Deptford Ironworks. The Hastings road was his favourite and he began running about 1840; he was one of the passengers on the *Automaton's* inaugural run to Cambridge. Few

Incomplete details of the two coaches credited to Hills of Deptford (1839-1841)

of his trips were recorded, but on one occasion he ran to Hastings and back in one day, with nine passengers and a crew of three. He was connected with the General Steam Carriage Company; in fact this firm probably worked his patents.

Two contradictory engravings exist of Hills' carriage*. This is not unusual, but in this instance no single item agrees. Although both have frames outside the rear wheels the horn-plates are upside down in one. One is a sporting-looking phaeton, the other a cumbersome double brougham. The author is of the opinion that there *were* two carriages. The evidence for this is that in 1839 *Philo Mechanicus*, a Luton reader of the *Mechanic's Magazine*, wrote saying he had visited a factory where two steam-carriages were almost complete, one to seat 15 and the other 20. The only people building at the time were Anderson, Roberts, Macerone and Hills. Being a Luton man he is more likely to have been to see Hills at

* Two cyls. 10 by 18 in., boiler pressure 70 lb., direct drive, 6 ft. 6 in. driving wheels, weight 4 tons.

Deptford than to Anderson in Ireland, or Roberts in Manchester. As for Macerone, it is unlikely he had enough money to build two carriages at once.

There now occurred an interesting episode ; on 21 November 1840 Sir George Cayley* drove his Gurney steam-car through a silversmith's window in Sloane Street. The engineer died of his injuries, and the Coroner put a deodand of £10 on the carriage, saying he considered them too dangerous to use. Apparently this was one of the Gloucester-Cheltenham drags, which had lain 18 months in Sir George's premises in Holywell Street, Millbank. On the day in question it was taken out to run to Hounslow for repairs. It worked well until Vauxhall Bridge Road was reached, when the driver in avoiding a boy thrown down in the path of the vehicle by another boy, ran on the pavement, straining the springs of the steering. In Sloane Street the steering began to give trouble, and the driver shut off steam, but the carriage swung round across the road and into the shop window, the engineer being trapped and badly cut by glass.

The figure chosen by fate to usher out the steam-carriage era was Sir James Anderson, who had been one of its first exponents. Since his collaboration with W. H. James he had been steadily building unsuccessful steam-carriages ; it is doubtful if any of them left his workshop. Now in 1839 random blasts of publicity in the scientific press heralded the construction of four hundred Anderson drags for the Steam Carriage & Waggon Co. of England, who had offices at 18 Moorgate Street.

By the end of March the *Mechanic and Chemist* was able to announce on the authority of the Secretary of the Company that the first drag was almost complete and would soon be seen in Dublin. The Journal described some of the trailers then being built by Dawson of Dublin, with six armchairs in the front body and ten in the rear body, the inside being furnished with a peculiarly-shaped table supplied with the newspapers of the day. The trailer also carried 14 passengers on the roof, and a cistern of water and coke for 10-20 miles in the front boot.

The *Cork Southern Reporter* had already visited Buttevant Castle, where Sir James was at work, and was told by him that " he had built 29 unsuccessful carriages to succeed with the 30th." The paper eulogised the workmanship of the machine, pointing out that it gave the lie to the suggestion that the Irish were inferior to the English in engineering skill. The intention was announced of running carriages from Birmingham to Holyhead to connect the packet boats with the London & Birmingham Railway. It is of interest that the London & Holyhead Steam Carriage Co. at about this time was investigating the possibility of laying " granite trams " for the steam carriages to run upon.

* Well known as a early aeroplane designer.

At the end of 1839 came the announcement that the engine, with a tender and diligence, had been shipped to England, and would shortly be showing its paces down Whitehall to the discomfiture of Hancock and Macerone. Next year, however, it became clear that the machine was still in Dublin, running along the Howth Road. Another Anderson drag was being built in Manchester, under the supervision of Richard Roberts, and ran its trials in 1840. But nowhere can any report be found of either appearing in London. Since such an event would certainly have been the subject of a defamatory letter from Macerone to the *Mechanic's Magazine*, it may be assumed it did not occur.

This was not, however, the end of Sir James. Interest in steam-carriages had fallen very low, yet still he worked on. In 1849 he was building a carriage for running between Hyde Park Corner and Hounslow. Its arrangement was novel : two horizontally-opposed cylinders drove a crank, connected with the wheels by gutta-percha belts and pulleys. Gear-change was effected by altering the pulleys, presumably on a fast-and-loose system as employed by Benz later. In 1850 the *Annual of Scientific Discovery* announced that Sir James Anderson had succeeded in perfecting his steam-carriage for common roads. But it seems that once again the signal of success turned into the will-o'-the-wisp from an Irish bog, for no more is heard of the Knight of Buttevant Castle.

In London, construction seems to have almost ceased. There is some evidence that a compressed-air-driven carriage built in Putney by a certain Baron von Rathem actually worked, but no details survive.

The embers of Georgian steam-carriage enthusiasm were now cold. The last expiring glow is a report in *The Mining Journal* of 1850 that a steam-carriage* had been invented " by a needy man in Tavistock." But two new types of common-road steamers had already been born : the light, fast-speed car pioneered in 1848 by Isaac Watt Boulton, and the farm-tractor by Ransomes, out of William Worby in 1842. In ten years' time the road locomotionists would be in full cry again, with the Marquis of Stafford, the Earl of Caithness and the Duke of Sutherland in the van.

To say, as some historians do, that common-road steam loco-motion died in 1838 is nonsense. For the romantic and gorgeously-accoutred steam stage-coach, indeed, the sands had run out ; but the same thing was happening to its horse-drawn competitor. The general tragedy of those whose livelihood depended upon the road transcends the mere disappointments of Hancock or Anderson. As the railways began to draw away the traffic, the old coaching hostelries went down and became derelict ; thousands of ostlers and stable-hands were thrown out of employment ; as the hutted camps of noisy quarrelsome navvies began to rise along the routes of projected railways, the character of England was changing. Had

* Two cyls. 4½ in. bore, weight 1½ tons.

PLATE V

*An engraving of Charles Dance's drag leaving the Wellington
Street station in London, probably in 1833*

*A coloured print dated June 1833 showing Hancock's "Enterprise"
omnibus*

PLATE VI

Walter Hancock's cars and 'buses 1828-38 : " trunnion " car,
" Infant I," " Infant II," " Era," " Enterprise," " Sun," second
" Era," alias " Erin," " Autopsy," " Automaton," German drag,
steam-gig, and 6-seat car. The "Sun" appears only in an untitled
print published by Conradi, and may not have existed.

PLATE VII

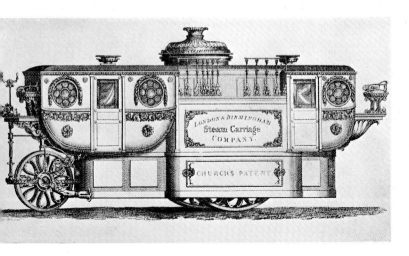

A contemporary drawing of Church's unsuccessful steam diligence of 1832.

A Macerone carriage illustrated by Dr. Dionysius Lardner in "The Steam Engine Explained" of 1840. Note fan driven by chain from rear wheel

PLATE VIII

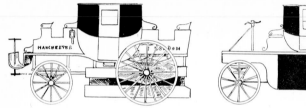

*Incomplete details of two compressed-air-driven carriages :
Mann's of 1830 (left) and S. W. Wright's of 1828 (right). Both
from contemporary prints*

*Top, left : Redmund's " Alpha " of 1834, from the " Mechanic's
Magazine.'' Right: Squire & Macerone carriage of 1832, from a
contemporary print. Bottom : a Scott Russell carriage of 1833,
with a tender*

*John Squire's "Albert" omnibus of
of 1843. From a contemporary prir.t*

the steam-carriage been able to retain even a little of the passenger traffic by competing on terms of equal service with the railways it would have been possible for the traditions of the coaching days to be preserved for the coming motoring age. As it was, the spirit of the travellers' inn flickered on meanly in the squalid " Railway Hotel." *The Artisan* of September 1843 attacked the railways for their " tyranny exercised in the transport of poorer passengers." " Now the road, with its fragrant hedgerows and picturesque cottages, is deserted . . . inns shut up . . . lives of thousands disarranged."

A self-moving fire engine built by Hodge in New York in 1840

§ 6 *The Birth of the Traction Engine* (1842-1868)

It is commonly stated that the traction-engine was inspired by agricultural interests. In fact, however, the stimulus came from three separate quarters. First, the military were interested in the possibilities. Admittedly some branches of the army showed no enthusiasm for the success of the traction-engine : but the needs of war were ever present in inventor's minds, and assistance was given from Woolwich. Secondly, agriculture appreciated the advantage of making their " portable engines " self-moving. These normally consisted of a locomotive-type boiler, with engine mounted above it, drawn about by horses. It was a simple matter to connect the crank-shaft by chain to one of the rear wheels, and this was done " unofficially " by some farmers themselves before self-moving engines became generally available. " Portables " normally had the cylinder above the firebox and the flywheel behind the chimney, and some of the very early tractions had the same arrangement, but to shorten the driving chain necessary this disposition was soon reversed. Thirdly, inventors were still hoping to introduce steam passenger carriages, and their plans for traction engines often had this directly in mind. Many engines did draw omnibuses overseas ; in this country such activities were virtually impossible by law, but a few experiments were tried.

In 1838 the *India Review* recorded experiments in drawing barges on Scotch canals by traction engine, but the earliest engine recorded in detail was that designed by William Worby* and built by Ransomes in 1842. It was shown at the Bristol Agricultural Society (probably in 1842, though John Head** states 1846). It had a vertical boiler and drive by pitch chain ; a horse in shafts at the front supplied the steering.

The next engine, designed by Robert Willis and built in 1849 by E. B. Wilson, of Leeds (for Ransomes), copied the railway locomotive very closely. It had a pair of cylinders† below the smoke-box and drew a tender. This was shown at Norwich in 1849 ; on test it ascended Freston Hill (1 in 11), and worked at several farms.

Several inventors more optimistic than practical now began to design farm-engines of a comprehensive type to do all sorts of jobs as well as haulage. A Canadian called Romaine, for instance, developed a cultivator of 14 h.p., two of which were built by Crosskills of Beverley in 1855. Usher was another such inventor. But the enormous weight of these steam factotums made them of little use. Of course steam-ploughing by winch had been well

---

* Grandfather of William Worby Beaumont, who delivered the Cantor Lecture on Mechanical Road Vehicles in 1896.

** Institution of Civil Engineers, 1873.

† 6½ by 10 in., heating surface 112 sq. ft., boiler pressure 45 lb., weight 2½ tons.

established before the coming of the traction engines. The plough was drawn across the field by winding the cable on and off a drum on the engine. Sometimes two engines stood at each side, sometimes an engine was employed on one side and an anchor on the other. In some systems the plough was reversible and ploughed in both directions, and in others it was drawn back clear of the soil. Early in the sixties the portable engines gave place to tractions for this work, and Fowler's double-engine system gained the ascendency, which it still holds to-day.

Whether on road or field, the problem with the traction engine was to get the driving wheels to grip the ground without digging in. W. Boydell had invented in 1839 a means of equipping wheels with flat hinged plates at the periphery, which formed in effect a self-laying roadway. Little notice was taken at first, though some guns were equipped with the plates and employed at the front in the Crimea. In 1855 he applied the system to the road engine. His first machine was built by Bach* of Birmingham, and his second in 1856 by Messrs. Burrell of Thetford, this being a four-wheeler with horizontal boiler at the rear and large " paddle-boxes " covering the wheels and porte-rails, as the hinged boards were termed. Another Boydell engine was mentioned in the *Engineer* of 4 April, 1856 ; the boiler and engine were built by Richard Garrett & Sons, of Saxmundham, and the wheels at the Woolwich Arsenal. " On Wednesday, April 2, the Messrs. Boydell & Glasier of the Camden Works, Camden Town, made several successful experiments with Boydell's Traction Engine, ordered by Lord Panmure. For some time Boydell's Endless Railway has been successfully applied to the wheels of gun-carriages and used in the Crimea. It is now proposed to draw such guns by traction engines." On 11 April 1856 the same journal reported experiments at Willesden in a field from which turnips had just been cleared. While returning to Camden the engine pulled out of a ditch a cart which had defied the efforts of seven horses to move it. In 1857 a three-wheeler on the same principle was built by Tuxfords : the Endless Railway Company was formed, and the system was hailed as the answer to the problem of steam on common roads.

In June 1857 W. McAdam spent eight days driving a Boydell engine† with trailers weighing 29 tons 85 miles from Thetford to Stratford. McAdam kept an extremely detailed log, such entries as " 3.47 : stopped for beer " being common. At 8.30 on the first evening he pulled into Bishop's Stortford for the night. As he turned off the turnpike into the inn-yard he stuck fast in a dung-heap, leaving the tail of his last wagon projecting into the roadway. " I put on double power," he reported " and took in the whole

---

* Credited by Galloway with building a steam carriage about 1840.

† Two cyls. 6 by 10 in., driving wheels 6 ft., weight 9 tons. Later engines had 7 by 12 in. cyls. and 5 ft. 6 in. drivers.

train, dispersing the dung-heap all round." "There was a loud shout from the bystanders," he added. This can well be believed : the dung-dispersing power of the six-foot drivers and porte-rails must have been considerable.

In the issue, not many Boydell engines were built, because running on a hard road broke up the porte-rails.

Boydell's chief competitor was William Bray of Folkestone. He began in 1857 by building a three-wheeled engine for use at Woolwich Arsenal, and shortly after R. & F. Hughes, of Deptford, began building his engines in fair numbers, both for home and overseas. Bray's wheel was an ingenious piece of work. Retractable " spuds " were fitted inside the rim, and by the action of an eccentric were pushed down through the rim as each came to the bottom ; the depth of penetration was controllable. The Bray Traction Engine Co. was formed, with the well-known D. K. Clark as consulting engineer.

The War Office were interested in both Boydell's and Bray's engines : some of the former's were employed in the Crimean War, and one was presented to the Pasha of Egypt. An eight-ton Bray engine hauling a 68-pounder gun was tested by the War Office in 1858 : speed averaged 2.272 m.p.h. ! The report stated that Boydell's engines were certainly the best, and one or two were put to work at Woolwich, but the experiments were not followed up with any energy. The German military expert, Lt./Col. Layriz reported " (in England) during the following long period of peace, and owing to the excessive extent to which economy was practised in military circles, the traction-engine found no admirers." Some Avelings and Fowlers were operated in the Russo-Turkish War, and Lord Roberts later found them very useful in South Africa.

Although these engines found their chief use in agriculture, efforts were made to popularise their use for goods haulage. On 25 February 1859 a Bray engine was to have made an exhibition run from King's Cross to Westminster with a load of 22 tons of coal. Owing to a drawbar failing, however, the engine made the run alone. At this time, too, a colliery near Manchester began sending their coal into town by road-engine, although the tolls payable were very heavy. Bray's system was not widely adopted because the engines damaged themselves by excessive shaking.

Thomas Aveling had been experimenting with chain-drive engines since 1858, and one was shown at Canterbury in 1860. Aveling's layout became standard for road engines. At first he had his single cylinder above the firebox, driving a crankshaft behind the chimney, fitted with a flywheel. Shortly after, however, he began employing a steam-jacketed cylinder behind the chimney, with the crankshaft fitted above the fire-box. He used fifth-wheel steering, and cast-iron wheels with ridges to increase adhesion. Later, he used an improved form of the Thompson rubber-tyred wheel, and also the Adams wheel in which a " tyre " of rubber between the spokes and the rim provided some elasticity. Two engines of his design, one built at his own works in Rochester, and the other by Clayton and Shuttleworth, were tested at Rochester in 1861. A curious feature of the Clayton engine was that the driving wheels were " those of the identical locomotive (bought from the South Eastern Railway), the boiler and cylinders of which went into the Arctic steamer *Fox*." Aveling's own engine* went through Strood and Rochester drawing threshing machines, and climbed gradients of 1 in 12 at 3 m.p.h. " A number of horses passed me but showed no sign of fear," reported the inventor.

The greatest argument of anti-locomotionists at this time was that horses, seeing the engine moving without apparent means, would panic. No doubt the use of horses in shafts to steer traction engines, widely practised, was partly on this account. One inventor proposed mounting a stuffed horse on the front of his engine.

Aveling's engines gained world-wide fame. M. Tresca, Sub-Director of the Conservatoire Imperial des Arts et Metiers, carried out trials with an Aveling engine named *La Ville de Senlis* at Beaurain, and in 1863 *Les Mondes* reported an Aveling in service between Berlin and Treptow. In 1868 one appeared in Havre towing an omnibus. Writing to the *Engineer* of 14 March 1862 Aveling referred to " the forty engines fitted with my patent locomotive gear now in constant work." It would seem that the Aveling engine, which was little more than a self-propelling " portable," had succeeded where the more elaborate machines had failed.

Richard Garrett of Leiston built his first " patent chain-drive engine " in 1858, though this does not seem to have been imme-diately successful except locally. The engine of Longstaff & Pullen (1859) behaved creditably. Trials took place at Euston in 1861 in the presence of the Marquis of Donegal. Drawing two wagons each loaded with ten tons of earth, the engine ran to King's Cross and up Pentonville Hill, scene of many of Hancock's exploits. It stopped at the chapel half-way up, and although full steam was applied it could not continue. One wagon was detached, and the other taken up easily : but at the top there was a loud crack and it was found that one of the driving wheels had fractured.

There were many lesser-known designers at work. A Mr. Daniel Adamson of Manchester built a road-engine in 1858, to the orders of Mr. Schmidt, to haul an omnibus : it is alleged that this took part in a race with one of Boulton's cars in 1867. Hornsby, Bonnel and Astbury built a two-cylinder " undertype " (engine below boiler instead of above it as usual) in 1862, and B. D. Taplin & Co. were advertising engines for sale at £590 in the same year. J. Taylor and

* 9 by 12 in. cyls., 5 ft. 6 in. wheels.

Co. of Birkenhead brought out a peculiar engine* called the " Steam Elephant," with short marine-type boiler and wheels with rubber cushions for the spokes to press upon. Tennant of Leith brought out a three-wheeled engine** in 1869, a powerful and heavy machine, which underwent test alongside a 6-ton Thompson engine : both hauled 34 tons up 1 in 25, although the Thompson had only half the weight on the drivers that Tennant's machine had. One or two road engines were specially designed for towing omnibuses. Adamson's engine has been mentioned, Ricketts' is mentioned in the next chapter. In 1860 Seaward & Co. built a drag for running between London and Leeds ; but there is no record of any of these in service. Small wonder, for in 1861 a general limitation of speeds to 10 m.p.h. (5 in towns) was applied, lowered in 1865 to 4 and 2 m.p.h.

Yet such was the demand by the farmers that the numbers of traction engines continued to swell rapidly. The South Kensington Exhibition of 1862 contained examples by Bray, Boydell, Taylor, Garrett, Taplin, Aveling, Marshall, Tuxford and Clayton & Shuttleworth. Fowlers began making steam ploughing engines in the same year. Other early makers included Wm. Allchin of Northampton, and Savage of King's Lynn. Design improved, worm and chain steering took the place of horse, fifth-wheel and front-platform steering. Two-speed gear drive became general, and by 1870 the traction engine had almost reached finality in development. Although many later engines were compounded, and various experiments were tried with unorthodox designs, in general the engie remained unchanged for the next sixty years.

* Two cyls. 5 by 10 in., 6 ft. driving wheels, weight 6 tons.

** Two cyls. 7¼ by 10 in., 5 ft. 8 in. wheels, weight 14 tons.

§ 7 *Light Steam-Cars* (1858-70)

The most interesting feature of early-Victorian road locomotion was the boom in light private cars which occurred in the 'sixties. Had it not been for restrictive legislation, this could have been the start of the vast expansion of motoring which actually occurred forty years later. With deference to the men who actually did launch large-scale motoring in 1898, those who would have launched it in 1862 were every bit as able. Consider four of the leading personalities :—

Alfred Yarrow, who as a boy fitted the first electric telegraph in London to keep in touch with a friend, and as a man had the temerity to escort Queen Victoria, unasked, with his torpedo boats when she reviewed the Fleet in the Solent.

R. E. B. Crompton, who was under fire in the Crimea at the age of eleven, left his mark on countless branches of engineering, and founded the famous electrical firm that bears his name.

Sir Richard Tangye, whose hydraulic jacks launched the Great Eastern and set up Cleopatra's Needle, and who built his large Cornwall Works in Birmingham only a few years after he had applied unsuccessfully for a job as stationmaster on the L.N.W.R.

Isaac Watt Boulton, carrying on the traditions of his famous ancestors.

There were patrons of motoring among the nobility who tried to do what then the Hon. C. Rolls and others did later, stamping the new sport with the cachet of gentility. Indeed since the score of motorists of the 'sixties known to history included the Earl of Caithness, the Marquis of Stafford and the Duke of Sutherland, their status proportionally was higher than it has ever been. No doubt had King Edward VII been a little older he would have been an eager patron also.

Unfortunately, reactionary influences gained the day, and initiative passed across the channel to the Comte de Dion and M. Amédée Bollée ; in England after a promising start the new light motors had to go " under cover," and only a handful were running after 1870.

I. W. Boulton seems to have been the first light car maker, for writing to *The Engineer* of 30 November 1894 he said, " It is 46 years since I first ran by steam on common roads." Of the six small vehicles he built in 1848 little is known.* He built a further car in 1860, and of this an illustration has survived. T. Boulton drove it from Ashton to Chester and back in 1867. Boulton was,

---

* One had boiler pressure 70 lb., two cyls. 3 by 6 in., and chain-drive. Another 130 lb. pressure, $2\frac{5}{8}$ by 9 in. cyls., weight 17 cwt., and was sold to a customer in Ireland.

of course, proprietor of Boulton's Siding at Ashton-under-Lyne, rebuilders and hirers of small railway engines.

In 1853, it is reported, Coley & Co., of the West London Ironworks, built a 3-cylinder direct-acting car, "which was not very successful."

The scene now changes to New York. Here in 1858 Richard Dudgeon, an Englishman, built a small steam-car, and drove around the capital with his top-hatted friends quite freely. E. G. Squier writing of it in the *Royal Society of Arts Journal* said " . . . although it met numberless carts on the journey, there was no collision " ; this might be regarded as faint praise, but was no doubt well-meant. The car was destroyed in a fire at the Crystal Palace, but a later (1868) Dudgeon car is still preserved at Belcourt. Also in America, Fisher, who had built cars in 1840 and 1853, built a third one in 1859. An engraving shows this to have a vertical boiler amidships, but details of drive are not given. In Denmark, a Mr. Jochumsen built a car about 1860.

Back in England, Ricketts, a Stony Stratford ironfounder, built his first car in 1859. It was for the Marquis of Stafford, and was designed by no less a personage than J. E. McConnell, Loco. Superintendent, Southern Division, London & North Western Railway. It had a short locomotive-type boiler facing to the rear, and seats for three in front ; transmission was by pitch-chain. A contemporary report stated : " This little engine started last Saturday from Messrs. Hayes works at Stony Stratford (where it had been undergoing some alterations) with a party consisting of the Marquis of Stafford, Lord Alfred Paget, Mr. J. E. McConnell, and two Hungarian noblemen. They proceeded to the residence of Mr. McConnell, and from there through the town of Stony Stratford, at a rapid pace, to Cosgrove Hall, the residence of J. C. Mansell Esquire, where they embarked on his steam pleasure-boat. They then returned to the Wolverton Railway Station, whence the engine proceeded back again to the works."

Ricketts built another car* in 1859, and sold it to the Duke of Sutherland ; His Grace was shortly to be seen driving furiously to any conflagration in the Greenwich area, followed by his self-propelled fire-engine.** This car was similar to the first, but had gear-drive. Next year Ricketts sold a third car† to the Earl of Caithness.

Of this car's doings a good deal is known, for the Earl was a great patron of science and his journeys were faithfully chronicled in the *Mechanic's Magazine*, the *Engineer* and even the *Illustrated London News*. When he ran in October 1860 from Inverness over the Ords to his seat at Barrowgill Castle, near John o' Groats, the

* Two cyls. 3 by 9 in.

** Probably built by Roberts (see p. 50).

† Two cyls. 3 by 7 in.

PLATE IX

A Bray traction-engine, drawn from an illustration in " The Engineer " 9 April 1858

A Tuxford Boydell-type traction-engine of 1857. From " The " Illustrated London News " of 12 December 1857

PLATE X

A peculiar car in which a steam man provided the motive power, built in Newark, New Jersey, about 1870. The boiler is inside his jacket.

The Earl of Caithness, with his wife and a friend, in their Ricketts car, built in 1860. From an engraving in " The Engineer " of 19 October 1869, prepared from a photograph taken at the time of the Earl's crossing of the Ords

PLATE XI

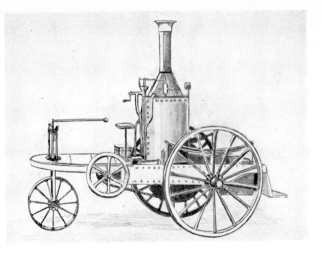

*One of Isaac Watt Boulton's small cars : this is
believed to have been built about 1860. Drawn from
a contemporary photograph*

ROAD LOCOMOTIVE, "CORNUBIA."

*Tangye's direct-drive steam car, from a pen sketch made at
about the time it was running*

PLATE XII

*The car built in 1861 by Carrett & Marshall for
Mr. George Salt of Saltaire. From contemporary
details in various publications which differ slightly
in minor points*

*A. F. Yarrow and friends in the Yarrow & Hilditch car. This print
appeared in " The English Mechanic " of 30 April 1869, some
eight years after it was built, with the title "Cowan's Improvements
in Steam Carriages on Common Roads "*

PLATE XIII

Roberts' self-moving fire-engine of 1862. From sketches in Young's " Fire-fighting "

R. E. B. Crompton's " Blue Belle," after rebuilding in 1865 in Rawalpindi. Lt. and Mrs. Crompton are here shown on their honeymoon, with a native chauffeur. From a photograph lent by Messrs. Crompton Parkinson & Co. Ltd.

PLATE XIV

H. P. Holt's car of 1866, with two cylinders driving each rear wheel. From contemporary data

Rhodes' car of 1863. From a drawing given by Fletcher

Chaplin's " patent traction carriage and winding engine," the " Hercules " built in 1862. From contemporary details

PLATE XV

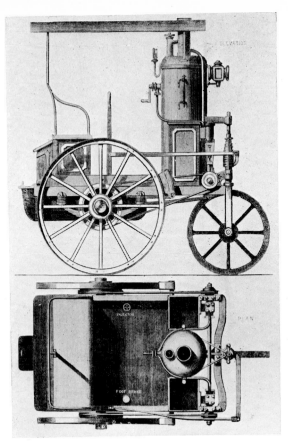

L. J. Todd's two-seater car of 1869. *From " The Engineer " of* 24 *Dec.* 1869

A car built by T. Cooke & Sons in 1865 *; from a photograph believed taken in the early 'seventies*

PLATE XVI

*Catley and Ayres' car of 1871. Copied from
a contemporary engraving*

*L. J. Todd's five-seater steam-car of 1870. Drawn
from contemporary details*

Engineer printed an engraving of three people sitting in the car, based on a photograph, explaining " the portraits are meant to be those of Lord and Lady Caithness and a friend who travelled with them. Our artist would have done greater justice to the originals had the photograph been clearer and more distinct."

Said the Earl : " Such a feat as going over the Ords of Caithness has never before been attempted by steam ; as I believe we rose about 1,000 ft. in 5 miles. On the level I got 19 m.p.h. Its cost of working is very small, ½d. to 1d. per mile. I passed the mail coach, Lord Lovat's carriage, etc. . . . the people seemed more frightened than the horses."

The Earl was presented with the honorary burgess ticket of Wick. The Countess said at the presentation ceremony : " . . . he, a Caithnessian, has taught the people that it is possible to cross the Ord in a steam-carriage (loud cheers). I am sure that as long as Caithness can boast of a steam-carriage propelled on its common roads, it has no cause to be ashamed, and may claim to itself what the Americans would style the character of a go-ahead country."

Her Ladyship must have been a more adventurous character than appears in the illustration (plate X); while admitting that the chauffeur probably did the heavy work, a three-wheeled vehicle with iron tyres running at 19 m.p.h., on a rough road, is not very comfortable. Probably there was a drawing-aside of skirts by some Scottish matrons ; the remark of a bystander at the trial voyage of Crompton's *Chenab* steamer, that " one did not usually see ladies riding on steam threshing machines," shows a proper Victorian spirit.

The *Year Book of Facts* for 1861 gives some details of the driving of the Earl of Caithness's car, interesting as an example of how difficult it must be to describe a car to anyone who has never seen one. " The driver sits on the right, resting his left hand on a handle at the end of a bent iron bar, passed below the front spring, to the jack in which the front wheel runs . . . placed horizontally before him is a small flywheel fixed on an iron rod, which passing downwards works at the lower end of a screw through one end of a lever attached at the other end to a strong bar that passes across the carriage and has fixed on it a drag for each of the hind wheels. Inside the carriage in a line backward from the right hand is placed a handle by which steam is let in, regulated, and shut off at pleasure." The carriage carried 170 gals. of water and 1 cwt. of coal, enough for respectively 12 miles and 20 miles.

Ricketts announced in the *Engineer* in 1860 that he was taking orders for cars at £180-200 apiece ; he was experimenting with a car having 250 lbs. boiler pressure and 800 sq. ft. of condensing surface, but this was not successful. In 1865 he built a direct-driven tractor with outside frame and locomotive-type boiler, shown in an engraving hauling a large omnibus labelled " London and North Western." There is no record of that railway adopting road feeder services at that time, but in view of Mr. McConnell's interest in Ricketts' work it is not impossible that something of this nature was tried. The engine itself went to Spain.

The year 1860 was not uneventful for common road locomotionists. Ricketts' and Boulton's cars were running, and Patterson and Louch & Messenger brought out one car each ; across the channel Lenoir had built the first practical petrol-engined car.

Patterson's car* was novel in having the boiler and engine mounted on the fore-carriage and swivelling with it. It was still in existence in 1897, though the engine had been removed to satisfy the police.

Louch & Messenger, who had a workshop at Swindon, designed their car† with a multitubular boiler set at a raking angle to expose more of the heating surface at low water-levels. There is a familiar ring about the inventors' story of an early trip. " In commencing the descent of a very steep hill, about half-a-mile long, one of the brake-blocks gave way, and the other not being sufficient to control it, the rapidly accelerating motion soon cause the machine to travel with tremendous velocity. Yet although the road was considerably circuitous, it was steered safely to the bottom." How many similar yarns were told between 1897 and 1910 ?

In 1860 the Frenchman Lenoir built a petrol-driven car, which has not received a tithe of the attention given to the doings of Drs. Otto and Daimler, but which was a pioneer effort of great importance. The engine was very like a high-pressure steam one, being single-acting and constant-volume. As the piston moved forward the mixture was drawn in ; at half-stroke it was exploded by the spark from a Rhumkorf coil ; the gases expanded until the end of the stroke, and the back-stroke cleared out the burnt gases. Otto's system of compressing the mixture before exploding was no doubt superior, but Lenoir's system drove a car 26 years before Otto's did so.

In 1861 the construction of cars continued, one each being produced by Crompton, Yarrow and Carrett ; all three had adventurous careers.

R. E. B. Crompton started building his car at the age of 16, in a small workshop at his home at Azerley. The boiler, however, was made in Leeds. He had been in correspondence with two other motorists, Cook of York (probably T. Cooke, see p. 41) and Salt of Saltaire (see p. 39). On Cook's advice he fitted a differential. His car was a four-wheeler with the boiler at the rear, drive being by leather belt. It ran trials in 1861 along the road between Azerley and Thievesgill, but apparently the boiler was not very efficient and the leather driving belts tore away. Two years later Crompton went to work under Sturrock at the Doncaster Works of the Great

* Two cyls. 3 by 6 in., boiler pressure 100 lbs.

† cyls. 3½ by 5 in., 120 lb., 3 ft. driving wheels, carried 40 gal. of water.

Northern Railway, and no doubt he gained useful experience, for when he joined the Rifle Brigade in 1864 and was posted to India, Ensign Crompton took his car with him and improved it in the Army workshops at his camp.

As improved the car was named *Blue Belle* and ran well. But hearing of the success of R. W. Thompson's rubber-tyred road steamers in England, he wrote to him, hoping to get a set of tyres for *Blue Belle* at a reasonable price. When he heard from Thompson of his success in running passengers by road steamers in Ceylon and the Dutch East Indies, Crompton suggested to Lord Mayo that they should be tried in India. A 6 h.p. engine was therefore ordered, and Lt. Crompton was appointed " Superintendent of the Government Steam Train." The story of this venture is told on pages 45-48. The *Blue Belle* must have been shipped back to England, for it was included in the Motor Museum in London when it opened in 1912.

Carrett & Marshall's car, nick-named the *Fly - by - Night* (it was in fact normal to drive by night now because of police activity), was designed by W. O. Carrett of Carrett, Marshall & Co., Ltd., for Mr. George Salt of Saltaire. It was a ten-seater* weighing five tons, with a short locomotive-type boiler at the rear and gear-drive. A feature was the special parallel-ruler suspension of the front forks, absorbing the shocks of the road. It was exhibited at the Agricultural Show at Leeds in 1861, and at the International Exhibition of 1862. Later, it was owned by F. Hodges and G. F. G. de Vigne of London ; after being repeatedly fined, de Vigne fitted a dummy hose and gave his friends firemen's helmets, and the police did not worry them again.

Alfred F. Yarrow, like Crompton, was an infant prodigy, who never became stale. From the age of fourteen, when he fitted up a device for his aunt to snuff her candle by remote control, to the height of his career as a torpedo-boat builder, his inventive energy knew no bounds. He and his friend J. B. Hilditch became experts in steam-ploughing at a very early age, and Yarrow (aged 18) was chairman at a meeting of the Civil & Mechanical Engineers Society at which Hilditch (aged 17) addressed the meeting on that subject. He was 19 when he designed his steam-car in collaboration with Hilditch. It was built by William Cowan of Greenwich, and exhibited at the 1862 Exhibition, being driven to South Kensington by Cowan himself. It took no prize, because (said Yarrow afterwards) the judge for carriages thought it was an engine, and the judge for engines thought it was a carriage.

The two friends drove it frequently from Greenwich to Bromley, with possible purchasers and other interested parties on board. The Yarrow & Hilditch Patent Steam Carriage Company was formed. One advantage of the design was that the rear wheels were carried inside the frame with such a narrow " track " that no

---

* Cyls. 6 by 8 in., heating surface 100 sq. ft. Driving wheels (steel) 4 ft. in diameter. Some authorities say ordered by Sir Titus Salt.

compensating gear was necessary for turning, although both were keyed to the axle. Considerable ingenuity was displayed in arranging that movement of the direct-driven rear wheels up and down should not interfere with the working of the valve-gear. The car ran a considerable mileage, mostly in North Kent, though one trip to Horsham is recorded. Cowan, writing to the *English Mechanic* of 30 April 1869, stated : " I have driven 6 miles in 22 minutes in the neighbourhood of Bromley . . . as comfortable and easy as a first-rate brougham." At the same time he gave details of the machine,* saying it could do 30 m.p.h. " but I consider that dangerous."

Some years later, writing to M. C. Le M. Gosselin of the Institute of Transport he said " ultimately I sold the car to someone in Ireland," adding some dimensions that do not tally with the earlier ages. This may account for statements that Yarrow built a second car with 6¾ cylinders weighing 2½ tons. This is not mentioned in his biography, which states that, seeing no fortune to be made on the road, he turned to steam-power on the water. It appears that one of the incidents affecting this decision was a meeting during a night drive to Bromley with a mounted policeman, who was thrown from his horse and suffered a broken leg. This caused an intensification of anti-motoring activity on the part of the police.

Meanwhile another of Victorian industry's eaglets, Richard Tangye, had come to the conclusion that since branch railways were proving unremunerative, light fast-speed road motors should be employed instead as feeders to the main lines. Tangye was yet another Cornishman, born in Trevithick's birth-parish of Illogan, near Redruth. His father had been born at Redruth, in a house past which Murdock's model car had run eighty years before. Tangye and his brothers had a granite slab set in the wall of Murdock's house, saying " William Murdock lived in this house 1782-1798 : made the first locomotive here, and tested it in 1784 . . ." By a curious coincidence they later set up their Cornwall Works in Soho, Birmingham, close by the historic foundry of Boulton and Watt, where Murdock lived in his later years.

The brothers were all ready to mass-produce cars : they built one, a direct-drive, four-wheeler† named *Cornubia*. Authority set its face against the project, however ; the " Red Flag " Act had been passed, limiting speeds to 4 m.p.h. " But for the action of a bovine Parliament," wrote Sir Richard in 1905, " the manufacture of motor cars would have taken root in England forty years ago, and foreign nations would have been our customers, instead of pioneers followed at a distance by ourselves." The *Cornubia* went out to India.

* 5-in. cyls., 3 ft. drivers, 3 in. tyre, boiler pressure 150 lbs.

† 5½ by 11 in. cyls., 3 ft. driving wheels, length 16 ft., width 5 ft. 9 in.

Nothing is known of the cars supposed to have been built in 1862, by Lee of Leicester and Wilkinson of Ashford, except their dimensions.* Little is known either of that** built by a Mr. Rhodes in 1863, though an illustration has survived. It probably did not run for very long, for Rhodes purchased H. P. Holt's car about 1867. Holt had built his car† in 1866 at Headingley, Leeds. It carried 6-8 passengers and ran at 15-20 m.p.h. The steam was superheated before exhausting, to avoid horse-frightening clouds of visible steam, a device used with indifferent success in early tram-engines.

A Mr. Hayball of Lymington, Hants, is credited by Fletcher with the building of a car*§ in 1864, but confirmation is lacking, though Fletcher is usually sound. A steam dog-cart was built by a Mr. Goodman in 1865, but nothing is known of its running. A. W. Forbes in Edinburgh built a car†* in 1866; the engine was fixed to the frame, with the boiler and body mounted above on springs : steam passed through a flexible connection. Since this avoided many complications in driving mechanism it is curious the idea was not more employed ; Lepape used it in his petrol car in 1898.

A car†† was built in 1865 by T. Cooke & Sons for "a private gentleman." It is said that the firm built three cars in all, two with engines of their own make and one with engines by Shand & Mason.

In the States, E. Ware of Bayonne built a small machine in 1867; it is interesting to note (plate XVII) that even then the "buggy"

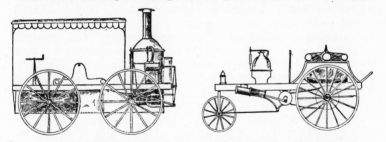

Incomplete details of Lt. Armstrong's car built at Rawalpindi in 1870 (left) and Goodman's steam dog-cart of 1865 (right)

characteristics that made the early Duryea petrol cars so different from our Continental patterns were present.

A mystery now presents itself. In December 1867 Mr. James Maynard was summoned at Greenwich Police Court for causing a locomotive engine to pass along a certain highway in the parish of

* Wilkinson : Cyls. 4½ by 12 in., 5 ft. wheels, boiler pressure 120 lbs. ;
Lee : Cyls. 4½ by 9 in., 6 ft. wheel, drive through spur gears.
** Two cyls. 3½ by 9 in.
† Two cyls. 3 by 6 in., heating surface 50 sq. ft., boiler pressure 250 lb.
§ Cyls. 4½ by 6 in., 12 seater, weighing 2 tons.
†* 4 by 10 in. cyls.
†† cyls. 5 by 6 ins., weight 2¼ tons.

Lewisham during prohibited hours (*i.e.*, between 6 a.m. and 10 p.m., an order relating only to the London area). He described his engine, which was a two-seater car. "The defendant, Maynard, pleaded ignorance of the order, and said that the makers of the cars supplied purchasers with a copy of the Acts of Parliament, which contained nothing about prohibited hours." He was fined 5s.; his chauffeur was also fined. Now what car was this? And what manufacturer was selling enough cars to make it worth while giving away copies of the Act of Parliament with them? One can only conjecture.

Certainly there was a great deal of activity at this time. "Sir," wrote some individual to the Editor of *English Mechanics* in July 1867, "I wish to possess a small road locomotive." In the next issue someone signing himself "H.H." (H. P. Holt?) sent a sketch of "one I think of making." Mr. W. S. Taylor wrote "seeing in your valuable paper a great deal of correspondence about road locomotives, I send a sketch of one I thought of making." These steam-car fans became rather mixed up with the people engaged in developing manumotive cars and the new velocipedes, and a steam-car might be referred to as a five-seat steam-cycle, or a steam velocipede as a road locomotive. (At this time traction-engines were referred to as Locomobiles, a French term which did not last long).

Correspondents to the mechanical and scientific journals were indefatigable in sending drawings of hand-and-steam-driven cars and cycles. The frontispiece to *English Mechanics* of 9 April 1869 showed a neat steam bath-chair gliding along a country lane, with the bewhiskered gallant driving apparently saying, "One moment, Lady Fanshawe, whilst I mend the fire." The question is: how many of these machines were actually put on the road? Very few of them were described in the serious engineering journals; rather they appeared to be the work of amateurs of the type who now

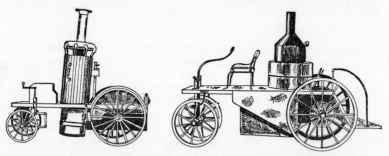

Light steam cars by Louch & Messenger (1860) left: and Knight (1868) right. From contemporary details

make model railway-locomotives with such gusto, and although some of the cars described and figured in the *English Mechanic* and other journals were clearly unworkable, others were quite sound. In view of the police attitude at the time, trials would necessarily have been *sub rosa*, and the fact that their running was in most cases not reported in the press cannot be taken as proof that they did not exist. Vehicles for which there is no satisfactory evidence of construction are, however, excluded from this survey.

Mr. Parker of Camberwell constructed a steam velocipede in 1867, in which special jets supplied a mixture of steam and air to the cylinder*. Steam could be got up in 6 minutes. An engraving shows the chassis only, and mentions " tests with the wheels off the ground," so possibly it never actually went on the road. J. H. Knight of Farnham, who was also active in the later internal-combustion era, built a four-wheeler in 1868. He ran this for five years, and sold it to a man who was experimenting with a new traction-wheel.

Experiments were not confined to this country. Ravel in Austria built an oil-fired steam car in 1868, and Michaux in France a steam-bicycle. In the U.S.A. Austin (1863), Lee & Larned (1863), J. A. Reed (1863), Curtis (1867), Clegg and Roper all built cars, and a clockwork omnibus ran in New Orleans in 1870 ; it proved too cumbersome.

As fast as one car-designer became discouraged, another took his place. G. Prew built a three-wheeler† which by June 1870 had already run 1,000 miles at a cost of 1d. per mile, carrying four persons (this figure included coal, oil and toll charges). It ran 62 miles from Birmingham to Gloucester in 7 hours.

Another inventor was L. J. Todd of Edinburgh, chiefly known from his omnibuses and trams. He gave details in the *English Mechanic* of 16 December 1870 of his " Steam cycle to carry five." This is one of the few cars of the period of which we have precise details. It had two cylinders $4\frac{1}{4}$ by 6 in., 24 sq. ft. of heating surface, oak wheels 3 ft. in diameter with $1\frac{3}{4}$ in. treads, connected to the axle by friction bands. " The driver sits on the front seat to the right, his right hand being in command of the steering handle and his left of the regulator. The person on the left fires the boiler and when necessary pumps up. The three passengers sit on the seat behind. The reverse gear can act most efficiently as a brake by bringing the handle a little way into back gear." Todd also seems to have built a two-seater with $2\frac{1}{2}$ by 4 in. cylinders.

Meanwhile in the Punjab, India, Rawalpindi was beginning to resemble Picadilly Circus. To Crompton's *Blue Belle* and Thompson's road-steamer was added a small car** built about 1870 by Lt. J. A. Armstrong, R.E. " The engine was made by myself with the help of a native smith and a boy's $3\frac{1}{2}$-in. lathe, and it consequently was not a particularly good job."

† Weight 15 cwt. Carried water for 10 miles, coal for 60 miles. Field boiler, 100 lb. pressure.

* Single 4 by 12 in. Water tube boiler.

** Two cyls. 3 by 6 in., drive through rocker bars.

Next year, in 1871, there was shown at the Yorkshire Agricultural Society's meeting a car† designed by Messrs. Catley & Ayres, a three-wheeler with vertical boiler and elliptical springing at front and rear. This is the last light car that falls within the ambit of the " first hundred road motors." It was not, of course, by any means the last light steam car. For thirty years to come steam was to hold its superiority in this field. In France, Amédée Bollée began building in 1872, and the possibilities were being keenly explored. In England, the dead weight of official opposition was poised to drop on any car-builder who raised his head, but models continued to appear at intervals, including the only one that is now still in running order, built by Greville in 1875. At the turn of the century light steam-cars began to be mass-produced in America, and many (' Whites ' and ' Locomobiles ') were running over here. But the purchase by Panhard & Levassor of the Daimler patents had sealed steam's fate, and it never really got a firm footing in the post-1898 motor age. For all that, building has not entirely ceased even to-day, though nowadays a car propelled by steam must be definitely " custom-built."

† Two cyls. $2\frac{5}{8}$ by $5\frac{3}{4}$ in., 150 lb., 19 cwt. tare, carried 20 gal. water, 2 cwt. coke.

PLATE XVII

The A.B.C. steam veloci-pede, featured by "The English Mechanic" of 9 April, 1869. It is un-likely that such a car was ever built.

The chain-driven car built in the U.S.A. by E. J. Ware in 1867 (see Appendix B)

STEAM CARRIAGE

SIR.—I enclose a photograph of a steam-carriage that has run 1,000 miles at the cost of 1d. per mile, carrying four persons, coal, oil and toll-

gates, making one farthing per mile for each person. It has run 62 miles in 7 hours—that is, from Birmingham to Gloucester, ascending and descending some of the steepest hills in the Midlands ; weight 15 cwt. The engines are driven by gearing 5 to 1 ; carries water 10 miles, coal for 60 miles; can do its 80 miles per day with ease. It has a patent " Field " boiler, 4-horse power ; general working pressure 50 lbs. on levels ; 90 to 100 up sharp hills ; never worked past 100 lb. steam.   G. PREW

From " The English Mechanic " of 17 June, 1870

PLATE XVIII

The Thompson-type road steamer " Advance," built in 1870 by Robey

Robey's " Advance " road steamer on trial service in Edinburgh with the omnibus " New Favorite," which Crompton later purchased for Indian service. From " The Illustrated London News " of 11 June 1870.

PLATE XIX

A reconstruction from working drawings of Todd's " Edinburgh " omnibus of 1871 ; it is not certain that this ever ran. The rear funnel was for ventilating the saloon

Nairn's 3-cylinder steam 'bus running on three willow-faced wheels, designed in 1870. It is not known whether it ran, but the very similar " Pioneer " ran in service between Edinburgh and Portobello. (From " The Engineer " of 28 January 1870)

PLATE XX

Aveling's first design of road roller. From
" The Engineer " of 4 October 1867

The Thompson road-steamer " Chenab " about to start from
Ipswich on a trial run in 1871. *Lt. Crompton is at the wheel.*
His wife sits in the saloon of the 'bus. From a photograph lent by
Messrs. Crompton Parkinson & Co. Ltd.

§ 8 *The " Road-Steamers "* (1867-72)

As early as 1859 " Caoutchouc* carriage wheels " were being advertised by a Mr. Davis of Lyons Inn, Strand. About 1867 R. W. Thompson, an Edinburgh engineer, first recognised the great benefit that might come from applying these new rubber tyres to heavy locomotion. The advantage would be two-fold : better adhesion for traction purposes, and protection from excessive jolting at high speeds. He used a continuous flat band of rubber loosely attached to the wheel, which in fact tended to creep round quite rapidly as the wheel went along, due to bagging-out more at the rear of the wheel than at the front. It was found to suffer badly from the road surface, and was fitted with loose metal plates sheathing it all round.

Thompson also designed the engine to use the tyres, a three-wheeler with " pot " boiler at the rear, and this " Road Steamer," as it was called, remained the same in general design for more than twenty years.

Left : Lotz's tractor built in Paris in 1868, and (right) Thompson's first road steamer of 1867

Possibly he was influenced by the work of Lotz in Paris, for the layout was similar to the passenger and goods drags being built by him, although the Lotz engine employed a single cylinder. Incidentally a Thompson engine was running in the Bois de Boulogne as early as 1868 !

The first engine** ran trials at Leith at the end of 1867: it had been built to haul a 35-seat omnibus, but proved much more powerful than necessary, easily moving very large boilers in Hawthorn's yard. It finally went to Java : meanwhile a heavier steamer* was put in hand for use in Ceylon.

---

* French for rubber.

** Two cyls. 7½ by 10 in., weight 6 tons.

The tyres for these tractors cost £150 per set, and wore out rather quickly (rubber loss was 10 per cent per thousand miles) ; but the improved performance they gave encouraged Thompson to continue.

Thompson's intention was to enable the engine to run at high speeds without damaging itself. But his pot-type boiler does not seem to have steamed well enough for continuous fast travelling. The first engine ordered for Lt. R. E. B. Crompton's Government Steam Trains, to transport goods and passengers in India (see p. 38) arrived there in 1870, and Lt. Crompton soon discovered the limited capacity of the boiler, particularly when using wood for fuel. This engine, a 6 h.p. one, was called *The Primer* (possibly a nickname due to its habits, though Crompton does not mention excessive priming). On one occasion at Allighur, Crompton was refused permission to unload the engine from the railway truck on which it was being carried, because freight charges had not been paid. He quietly got up steam and drove it off the truck and out of the station compound with the stationmaster at his heels, which argues a fair acceleration. However, when Crompton came to England, met Thompson, and gave orders for four more engines, he frankly told Thompson he did not care for his " pot " boiler, and had Field boilers fitted to all but the first of the new engines.

Instructions were given to Robey of Lincoln to build the first engine, called the *Advance*. This was substantially the same as the 1867 one. It was probably this engine which was enthusiastically described in an Edinburgh journal ; as it "ran down to the Portobello shore . . . it seemed impossible it could work on such soft sinking sand, but on it rushed through all, over some quicksands, ran into the sea and along its edge in every direction in the most wonderful manner." In fact, in its elephantine ballet-dance the 9-ton steamer probably did not exceed ten miles per hour.

But the *Advance* went through its first paces at Lincoln, and was reported in the *Lincoln Gazette* of 3 December, 1870 :—

" PUBLIC TRIAL OF A ROAD STEAMER.—Ever since railways have been introduced into this country, a desire has been felt by the most eminent engineers to construct a road steamer, adapted for districts which are out of the line of railway communication. Many attempts have been made in this direction, but the traction-engines (several of which have been manufactured in this city) have hitherto failed to meet equally the requirements of the civil engineer and the agriculturist, mainly because it has been found impossible to overcome the inqualities of a common road. This problem has now been satisfactorily solved by Mr. R. W. Thopmson's patent india-rubber tires. The tires, 14 in. broad, are protected by chain steel plates 18 in. in width, and the surface of the wheel next the ground is flattened to the length of 22 in., thus offering a surface contact of $2\frac{3}{4}$ sq. ft. The first experiment was to show the adaptability of the road steamer for passenger traffic. Shortly before one o'clock it was attached to an omnibus and a drag, in which 40 gentlemen had seated themselves, and steamed along the Canwick Road up Melville Street, Broadgate, and the New Road, at the rate of from four to five miles an hour. There was not the slightest jolting in the conveyances, even when passing over the mount sorrel pavement, and an easier and more comfortable ride could not possibly have been enjoyed. The steamer gallantly faced the steep acclivity presented by the New Road, ascending it without a single stoppage. On reaching the junction of the Greetwell and Wragby Roads, opposite the Peacock, the steamer and train were turned round for the return journey, the radius of the circle being only about 18 ft. On arriving at the southeast corner of Mr. Tweed's garden, ' slippers ' were attached to the conveyances, and the engine steamed down the incline at the rate of nearly ten miles an hour, the greatest velocity being reached at the awkward turning at the top of the New Road. A portion of the passengers appeared to be somewhat alarmed at the pace at which the steamer was travelling, but to show that it was completely under control, its progress was instantly arrested at the very steepest point, where the gradient is no less than one in nine. The second experiment was to show the capacity of the steamer for drawing goods traffic on common roads. To do this, the steamer was attached to two trucks, specially constructed for this particular traffic, weighing three tons each. . . . It was really wonderful to see how completely it was under the control of the driver, Mr. Stanger, Instructor of the new corps of engine drivers at the Royal Arsenal, Woolwich. ' Knowledge is power,' and the ponderous steamer obeyed the will of its driver as readily and as easily as a willing human being could possibly have done. The engine next steamed a measured mile, on the grass, completing the distance in exactly seven minutes, being at the rate of eight-and-a-half miles an hour."

The reference to passenger traffic will be noted. Engravings show the *Advance* at Edinburgh, in company with a 65-seat two-wheeled rubber-tyred omnibus, built by Robeys and named the *New Favorite*, lettered " Edinburgh and Leith." While no doubt it did work there experimentally, the same bus next appears behind the *Chenab* (Crompton's third engine, by Ransomes) on test, lettered " Jhelum and Rawul Pindi." Crompton had bought it for his road trains, and about this time he took in it several august personages, including the Dukes of Devonshire and Sutherland and Sir John Fowler, for " a bit of speed work and manoeuvering" near Stafford Railway Station. Driving *Chenab*, Crompton managed to make his passengers seasick. Because of weaving and hunting this two-wheeled design gave less satisfaction than the old four-wheeled omnibuses used in the bullock trains, some of which Crompton pressed into service for his steam trains in India.

With Ransomes' second engine, the *Ravee**, Crompton made a trip from Ipswich to Edinburgh, also towing the omnibus. On the

* Two cyls. 8 by 10 in., 6 ft. driving wheels, 177 sq. ft. heating surface.

narrow fen roads round Peterborough with drain-ditches either side there were many escapes from disaster : Crompton on one side and his wife on the other kept close watch lest the wheels should start a slide into the ditch. At Edinburgh the *Ravee* performed in front of R. W. Thompson in his invalid-chair. Returning, near Barham a bevy of mill-girls in night-dresses clambered on the omnibus and a mile or so further on, in spite of warnings, jumped off facing backwards, resulting in " a ludicrous spectacle."

The engines began to arrive (in parts) at Rawalpindi in March 1872, the crates being hauled up from the river by *The Primer*. In the same year *Chenab*, *Ravee* and *Indus* were on manoeuvres.

The *Indus*, with its tare reduced to 8½ tons by placing the water supply in the tender, drew 64 tons 6 cwt. up a gradient of 1 in 33 at 5 m.p.h. When in service, there were stations of fuel every 14 miles and of water every 7 miles. Crompton was handicapped by shortage of rolling stock. He had only one heavy omnibus*, three lighter ones off the bullock trains, four six-ton wagons and two smaller ones.

Ransomes built another steamer,† called *Sutherland*, in 1871, for agricultural use by the Duke. Burrell of Thetford built four for service in Crete and Russia, and in 1872 began a variant of the design having a locomotive-type boiler facing the rear. One** for the Turkish Government had the boiler inclinable so that it could work on steep grades without uncovering too many tubes. J. & T. Dale had built two similar but lighter machines in 1868 for the New Zealand Government. These were fitted with Nairn's elastic wheel, but Nairn's system, although originally it employed rope in place of rubber to save cost, later seems to have been virtually the same as Thompson's ; he may have taken it over from the latter, who was a sick man and relied on his wife to run the business side of his venture.

The degree of success of the Thompson steamer is not sufficiently recognised. It was no flash in the pan. Robeys were still building them to order in 1891, having by then made 50 to 60 such engines. Mr. Harry Stanger (p. 47), a traction-engine driver, told the Institution of Civil Engineers in 1890 :" any one who has tried to get an ordinary engine out of a dirty occupation road through a narrow gate could understand the difficulty of just hitting the right place between the gate-posts : but with a road steamer the driver would be able to steer his engine straight through." They were, however, more expensive than ordinary traction engines. Capt. Losada, manager of the Glasgow Tramways, stated in 1879 that the Thompson

* There were two in the English tests ; one probably belonged to Robey and did not go to India.

† Two cyls. 6 by 10 in., driving wheels 5 ft. by 19¼ in., heating surface 140 sq. ft., weight 10½ tons.

** Two cyls. 7¼ by 10 in., heating surface 231 sq. ft., weight 8 tons.

engines were so fully established in that town that " no single article weighing over 10 tons was ever moved except by one of them."

Leading naturally out of the road steamers comes the story of the steam omnibuses of L. J. Todd and Nairn, both engineers of Leith. Here was an attempt to introduce fast-speed engines built integral with the 'bus, instead of towing it. Todd's *Pioneer* three-wheeled omnibus,* seating 50 passengers, ran for four months during the summer of 1871, between Edinburgh and Portobello, a total of 952 trips. Working expenses averaged £12 per week, and earnings £20 per week. It was 22 ft. 6 in. long, 6 ft. 6 in. wide, and ran on three 40 in. wooden wheels with rubber tyres. There were troubles : it proved liable to overturn, back-pressure developed in the engine, and because the chimney passed through the saloon the interior became uncomfortably hot.

Meanwhile Todd had designed a four-wheeler on somewhat similar lines, called the *Edinburgh*, and in 1872 designs were out of an *Edinburgh* by Nairn, though there is no proof that either of these ran in service. They cannot easily be confused, although the body-work was somewhat similar ; Todd's had two funnels like a ship, raking aft (the rear one was for ventilation only), and final drive by counter-shaft and coupling rod. Nairn's *Edinburgh*, on the other hand, had a single horizontal flue running along the roof and exhausting at the rear, and direct drive. Todd's was a four-wheeler and Nairn's a three-wheeler.

Todd also designed a drag called the *Centaur* " for passenger and mail traffic beyond the reach of railways," in 1872, but there is no record of its running. Nairn advertised his buses for sale " with steam up at Leith," but in fact the coming of the steam tram, on which Todd was also working, removed the incentive to develop the steam-'bus. The road had some supporters, however. " The Harmonious Blacksmith," writing to the *English Mechanic* of 12 July 1872, said : " the owners of a carriage which runs on common roads have the great pecuniary advantage of not having to pay for the making of the road. Under our enlightened commercial system, which delegates the making of our highways—railways and tramways are nothing else—to private enterprise, the proprietors defray the cost, charging higher fares than would be required did society make and mend its own ways."

* Three cyls. $7\frac{1}{2}$ by $10\frac{3}{4}$ in., weight in working order 11 tons.

§ 9 *Specialised Road Engines*

One Perkins had the idea of copying the adaptability of the horse, and built a " steam-horse " with one wheel for fitting to the fore-carriage of carts (a system used for electric cabs in Paris thirty years later). The " horse " could only manage 3 m.p.h. on test attached to a 3-ton van. Sir F. Bramall stated in 1894 that this engine was still in use at the Gypsum Works at Battle, but Beaumont says it was sent to Belgium.

The history of mechanical road traction has, of course, been strongly influenced by the state of the roads themselves. No attempt was made to suit road-surfaces to steam traction : naturally, since the object of the authorities was to discourage their use. In the sixties, however, the growth of heavy horse-drawn traffic forced the authorities to take some action. It appears that the first call for steam-rollers came from Calcutta, the machines being built by Clark & Baths, of Birmingham, in 1864. Aveling interested himself in the matter, and supplied a roller in 1867 to Liverpool ; in the following year the Islington Vestry took delivery of a 25-ton Thompson roller. It was also at Islington that an Aveling roller was tested in 1870. The front and rear rollers together gave a total roll of six feet : the weight was 15 tons. An expert wrote : " The Islington Vestry have at last done what all the Metropolitan local boards ought to have done years ago : namely, obtained a steam road-roller for use on the roads under their charge . . . we can only hope that the example so tardily set by the Islington Vestry will be followed by their still more tardy brethren." A little later an Aveling roller was successfully used to break a strike of navvies in the Old Kent Road.

A branch of the public service that might have been expected to take up fast-speed steam-motors was the fire service. But not so. Paul Hodge in American had built a self-propelling steam fire-engine in 1840, and in this country Mr. W. Roberts in 1862 built one* capable of 18 m.p.h. It ran a good deal around the London docks, more on general pumping duties than on fire-fighting ; but the idea was not taken up until Merryweathers began building self-moving steam fire engines thirty years later.

There was a natural temptation to make the newly-developed traction engine into an all-purpose machine, and several makers fitted small cranes to the fore-part ; winching gear on the driving axle was fairly general, and the flywheel itself provided means for a power take-off for driving machinery. In 1862 Alex. Chaplin & Co. built a " Combined Traction Carrying and Winding Engine "† called *Hercules*, with vertical boiler at the rear and a large platform-body in front, fitted with a crane and winch.

* Two cyls. 6 by 12 in., 5 ft. drivers, 7½ tons (Plate XIII).

† Two vertical cyls. 7 by 14 in., drive through spur gearing.

This completes the tale of the first hundred road motors. The division is an arbitrary one, however. The next hundred follows straight on, beginning with Randolph's steam 'bus of 1872. A handful of inventors still struggled on against repressive legislation and public indifference. Their efforts would be crowned by victory in 1896, with the " Red Flag Act " repealed, but for steam it would be a Pyrrhic victory, petrol stealing most of the fruits.

The claim is sometimes made that no progress in road motors was made after Hancock went off the road. This is not entirely true; for instance the Field-boilered road-steamer of 1871 was a far more capable machine than the drags of earlier days. But it cannot be denied that between Hancock's *Automaton* and Todd's *Pioneer* there was certainly less progress than between their contemporaries on the railway, Stephenson's *Patentee* and Stirling's 8-foot " singles." The answer is that the poor quality of the roads checked incentive to increase weight, power or speed of road vehicles. The invention of the pneumatic tyre at the end of the century made higher speeds possible on the same indifferent roads, and triggered off a series of inventions whereby motor vehicles soon became lethally fast. But let us not look down upon the steam motorist of the 'sixties. With his two-cylinder " simple " engine and conventional boiler he had a sound and trouble-free machine. Not for him the frequent stoppages that made life so difficult for the driver of the complex and unpredictable petrol motor of the late 'nineties. He liked to jog along at a steady twenty, and he only asked for a clean brook by the roadside every twenty miles, and no over-zealous police constables. If he could see, as we can, the accelerating journey of the motor car through decade after decade towards final mass-production, would he not argue that in many ways it is better to travel than to arrive ?

APPENDIX A

List of the First Hundred Road Motors

Compiled from the best available evidence. Vehicles numbered almost certainly were built, although they may not have run successfully. Vehicles for whose existence there is only slight evidence are included, but not numbered. Mere patents or designs are not included. To avoid crossing the frontier into the realm of farm and industrial machinery, traction engines, self-propelling fire-engines, etc., are not numbered, although they are included for interest's sake. The term " tractor " implies an engine built for towing but not for stationary working, and " drag " a similar vehicle specifically designed to tow light passenger carriages. " Tractions " were designed largely for stationary working, though many of course ran long distances on the roads. A " road steamer " was a specialised form of tractor whose purpose is explained in the text. Again for interest, the best-known foreign cars and other engines are also included.

No.	Designer	Builder (if not same)	Type of Vehicle	Where built	Date
	Cugnot		wagon	Paris	1769
	Cugnot		wagon	Paris	1771
	Dallery		amphibian	Amiens	1780
	Symington		model ? carriage	Edinburgh	1876
1	**Fourness**		tractor	Otley ?	1788
2	**T. Allen**		carriage	London	1789
	N. Reed		carriage	Springfield, U.S.A.	1790
3	**Trevithick**		carriage	Camborne	1801
4	**Trevithick**		carriage	Camborne	1803
	O. Evans		amphibian	U.S.A.	1804
	de Rivaz		car	France	1807
	Bozec		car	Prague	1815
	Medhurst		carriage ?	London ?	1819
5	**Griffiths**	Bramah	carriage	Birmingham	1821
6	**S. Brown**		carriage	London	1823
7	**D. Gordon**		carriage		1824
8	**Burstall and Hill**		carriage	Leith	1824
9	**Burstall and Hill**		carriage	Leith	1825
10	**Gurney**		carriage	London	1825
11	**Gurney**		carriage	London	1826
12	**Anderson and James**		carriage	London	1826
	Neville		tractor ?		1827
13	**Nasmyth**		carriage	Edinburgh	1827
14	**R. Napier**		drag	Glasgow ?	1827
	Pecqueur		wagon	Paris	1828
15	**Hancock**		carriage	Stratford	1828
16	**Gurney**		drag	London	1829
17	**Fraser**		carriage		1829
18	**Summers and Ogle**		carriage	London	1829
19	**Anderson and James**		drag	London	1829
20-2	**Gurney**		3 drags	London	1830
23	**Hancock**		omnibus	Stratford	1830
24	**Gibbs and Chaplin**		tractor		1830
25	**Mann**	Fordham ?	carriage		1830
26	**Hancock**		omnibus	Stratford	1831
27	**Summers and Ogle**		carriage	Southampton	1831
28	**Squire and Macerone**		carriage	Paddington	1831
29	**Gibbs and Applegarth**		drag		1832
30	**Church**	Bramah	carriage	Birmingham	1832

No.	Designer	Builder (if not same)	Type of Vehicle	Where built	Date
31	Squire and Macerone		carriage	Paddington	1833
	Palmer		carriage ?		1832
32	R. Roberts		drag	Manchester	1833
33	Heaton Bros.		drag	Birmingham	1833
34	Dance	Maudslay & Field	drag	London	1833
35-6	Hancock		2 omnibuses	Stratford	1833
37-42	Scott Russell		6 carriages	Edinburgh	1833
43	Yates & Smith		carriage		1834
	Dietz		drags	Paris	1834
44-5	Hancock		2 omnibuses	Stratford	1834
46	Redmund		omnibus	London	1834
47-50	Hancock		gig, omnibus and 2 drags	Stratford	1835
	Millichap		carriage	Birmingham	1837
51	Hancock		car	Stratford	1838
52	Anderson		drag	Ireland	1840
53	Anderson	R. Roberts	drag	Manchester	1840
54-5	Hills		2 carriages	Deptford	1840
	Hodge		fire engine	U.S.A.	1840
	Fisher		carriage	U.S.A.	1840
56	Macerone	Beale	carriage	Greenwich	1840
	W. Worby	Ransomes	traction	Ipswich	1842
57	Squire		carriage	London	1843
58-63	I. W. Boulton		6 cars	Ashton-under-Lyne	1848
64	von Rathem		carriage	Putney	1849
65	Anderson		carriage		1849
	Willis	E. B. Wilson	traction	Leeds	1849
	Coley		traction		1849
	Fisher		car	U.S.A.	1853
	Coley		car ?	West London	1853
	Romaine	Crosskills	cultivators	Beverley	1855
	Boydell	Bach	traction	Birmingham	1855
	Boydell	Burrell	traction	Thetford	1856
	Bray	Hughes	traction	Deptford	1857
	Boydell	Tuxford	tractions	Boston	1858
	Dudgeon		car	New York	1858
	Clayton & S.		tractions	Lincoln	1858
66-7	McConnell	Ricketts	2 cars	Stony Stratford	1859
68	McConnell	Ricketts	car	Stony Stratford	1860
69	Louch & Messenger		car	Swindon	1860
	Jochumsen		car	Denmark	1860
70	Patterson		car		1860
	Lenoir		car	France	1860
	Longstaff & Pullen		traction		1860
71	I. W. Boulton		car	Ashton-under-Lyne	1860
	Aveling		tractions	Rochester	1860
	Robey		tractions	Lincoln	1860
72	Crompton		car	Azerley	1861
73	Carrett	C. & Marshall	car	Leeds	1861
74	Yarrow & Hilditch	W. Cowan	car	Greenwich	1861
	Taplin		traction		1862
	N. Roberts		fire engine	Millwall	1862
	Clayton		traction	Lincoln	1862
	Chaplin		crane wagon		1862
75	Wilkinson		car	Ashford	1862
76	Tangye		car	Birmingham	1862

No.	Designer	Builder (if not same)	Type of Vehicle	Where built	Date
77	Rhodes		car		1862
	Allchin		tractions	Northampton	1862
	Fowler		tractions	Leeds	1862
78	Lee		car	Leicester	1863
	Austin		car	U.S.A.	1863
	Taylor		traction		1864
	Brown & May		traction	Devizes	1864
79	Hayball		car	Lymington	1865
80	Ricketts		drag		1865
81	Goodman		car		1865
82	Cooke		car	York ?	1865
83	Holt		car	Headingley	1866
84	Forbes		car	Edinburgh	1866
	Lotz		omnibus	Paris	1866
	Michaux		bicycle	France	1867
	Parker		car ?	Camberwell	1867
	Ware		car	Bayonne, U.S.A	1867
85	Thompson		road steamer	Leith	1867
	Ravel		car	Austria	1868
	Dudgeon		car	New York	1868
86	Prew		car	Birmingham ?	1868
87	Knight		car	Farnham	1868
88-9	Nairn	J. & T. Dale	road steamers	Kirkcaldy	1868
	Lt. Armstrong		car	Rawalpindi	1868
90	Tennant		road steamer	Leith	1869
91	Todd		car	Leith	1869
92	Thompson	Robey	road steamer	Lincoln	1870
93	Thompson	Burrell	road steamer	Thetford	1870
94	Perkins		steam horse		1870
95	Nairn		omnibus	Leith	1870
96	Catley & Ayres		car	York	1870
	Savage		traction	King's Lynn	1870
	Todd		omnibus ?	Leith	1871
97-100	Thompson	Ransomes	road steamers	Ipswich	1871

APPENDIX B

Through the kindness of Mr. P. S. de Beaumont, of the Antique Automobile Club of America, the following details of some early American cars are appended :

S. H. ROPER.

From *The Scientific American* for November 28 1863 : An ingenious mechanic, Mr. S. H. Roper, of Roxbury, Massachusetts, has invented and put into operation a new steam wagon or buggy for common roads. It is thus described :—An ordinary 4-wheel carriage has a boiler, of about 16 in. diameter, in the rear, with the lever regulating the steam and speed extending over the seat in front. Beneath this boiler is the furnace, and in the rear of the boiler is a small water tank. The steam guage is on a level with the driver, and he can at a glance ascertain the amount of steam pressure. The whole machine is of 2 h.p. Two persons take their seats in the carriage, and off it starts, the driver guiding with one hand the front wheels, by means of a crank, and with the other hand he can regulate the speed of the engine or stop the carriage in less time than a pair of horses can be brought to a halt. Coal sufficient for one day's running can be carried beneath the seat of the carriage, and although the speed attained is that of the fastest horse, the expense of running the carriage is estimated at one cent per mile, while in operation, with the additional virtue of not costing anything in the way of feed and stabling when not in use. Lately, when the carriage was exhibited, the engine carried but 15 and 20 lbs. of steam, and yet it taxed the powers of the horses present to keep pace with its speed. The carriage and engine do not weigh more than 700 lbs. No difficulty was experienced in turning sharp corners or in backing.

E. J. WARE.

From *The Scientific American* of 19 January 1867 : The appearance of the machine in one form is seen by the engraving. As a carriage it presents a graceful appearance. The boiler is hung between the forks of a frame of steel, which meet on the forward axle and thence backward diverge, holding the boiler suspended in the triangle thus formed. This frame of steel, edge up, is twisted a half-turn on each side of the boiler, thus acting as a spring. The engines work on an incline and drive a shaft with a chain wheel, which, by a machine chain, rotates the driving shaft and wheels. The engine is intended to give three revolutions to the first shaft to one revolution of the driving wheels, thus gaining power for ascending inclines. The difference can be multiplied to nine times. A lever in front of the driver's seat serves, by a simple mechanism, to guide the machine when used as a carriage, and a rod with handle connected to the engine shaft readily reverses the motion of the engine.

As will be seen, the machine is a complete engine in itself, capable of doing the work ordinarily done by the portable or stationary engine, and also adapted for locomotion. The inventor is confident that his machine can be made a success, as all those he has yet built perform their work admirably.

For further particulars address Elijah Ware, Bayonne, N.J.

T. BLANCHARD, of New York published in 1825 patents covering the application of gears to rapid alteration in propelling-power and speed of road vehicles.

A. B. LATTA, published in 1855 patents covering steam carriages with hind wheels capable of revovling independently. Drawings show a three-wheeler with vertical boiler and direct drive by outside cylinders.

J. K. FOSTER of New York, published in 1861 patents covering a system of radius-rods, etc., enabling the springs of a steam-carriage to flex more freely without strain on connecting-rods. Drawings show a four-wheeler with vertical boiler and direct drive from outside cylinders.

Many other patents covering steam-cars were taken out in the early 'sixties, but most of them seem never to have been put to practical use.

Page Fifty-five

BIBLIOGRAPHY
(All these works include some source material)

LT./COL. F. MACERONE *A Few Facts About Elementary Locomotion*, 1834 ; *Memoirs of his Life and Adventures*, 1838.

A. GORDON. *History of Steam Locomotion on Common Roads*, 1834.

WALTER HANCOCK. *A Narrative of Twelve Years' Experience*, 1824-36. John Weale, 1838.

DIONYSIUS LARDNER. *The Steam-engine Explained*, Taylor & Walton, 1840.

LUKE HEBERT. *The Engineer's & Mechanic's Encyclopaedia*, 1860.

C. F. T. YOUNG. *The Economy of Steam Power on Common Roads*, 1860.

A. F. YARROW. *On Steam Carriages.* Trans. Soc. Engineers, 1862.

A. AINE. *Machines Outils et Appareils.* Annually, esp., 1871.

R. L. GALLOWAY. *The Steam Engine*, MacMillan, 1881.

W. FLETCHER. *The History and Development of Steam Locomotion on Common Roads*, Spon, 1891.

THURSTON. *A Manual of the Steam Engine*, Wiley, 1892.

SIR F. BRAMALL. *Reminiscences of Steam Locomotion on Common Roads*, Section G, British Association, 1894.

RHYS JENKINS. *Early Mechanical Carriages*, Antiquity, 1896. *Motor Cars*, 1902.

W. WORBY BEAUMONT. *Mechanical Road Carriages*, Cantor Lectures, 1896.

A. R. SENNETT. *Carriages Without Horses Shall Go*, Whittaker, 1896.

E. G. SQUIER. *Steam Carriages on Common Roads*, Society of Arts Jnl., VI 588, XIII 115, XXI 411.

LT./COL LAYRIZ. *Mechanical Traction in War*, Sampson Low, 1900.

W. FLETCHER. *English and American Steam Carriages and Traction Engines*, Longmans, 1904.

G. LAVERGNE. *The Automobile*, Cassell, 1901.

RHYS JENKINS. *Comparative Bibliography of Power Locomotion on Highways*, 1896.

GARDNER D. HISCOX. *Horseless Vehicles.* N. W. Henley & Co., New York, 1901.

J. NAPIER. *Life of Robert Napier*, Blackwood, 1904.

S. SMILES. *Life of James Nasmyth.*

RICHARD TANGYE. *The Rise of a Great Industry*, Partridge, 1905.

R. E. B. CROMPTON. *Reminiscences*, Constable, 1928.

ARTHUR POUND. *The Turning Wheel*, Doubleday Doran, 1934.

R. H. CLARK. *Steam Engine Builders of Norfolk*, Privately, 1948.

(showing approximate dates at which they were active)

(Roman numerals refer to Plates.)

PUBLISHED BY THE OAKWOOD PRESS, TANGLEWOOD, SOUTH GODSTONE, SURREY